COMPANION WORKBOOK

Is it Me?

MAKING SENSE OF
YOUR CONFUSING MARRIAGE

NATALIE HOFFMAN

FLYING FREE
M·E·D·I·A

Copyright © 2019

Companion Workbook: Is It Me? Making Sense Of Your Confusing Marriage

Natalie Hoffman

FLYING FREE
M · E · D · I · A

Flying Free Media
13090 Crolly Path
Rosemount, MN 55068

FlyingFreeNow.com

ISBN: 978-1-7328943-2-7 (print)

Ordering Information:
Special discounts are available on quantity purchases by corporations,
associations, and others. For details, contact
the publisher at the address above.

Publishing and Design Services: MartinPublishingServices.com
Editor: HEDUA, LLC
Author Photo: Raquel Martinson

Contents

Dear Friend,

You are holding this workbook in your hands because you're ready to take your healing to a new and deeper level. Maybe you've already read *Is It Me? Making Sense of Your Confusing Marriage* or listened to it on Audible, and now you want to spend some time processing what you read. Or maybe you purchased the book and workbook together, and you're going to go through it with some other women on the same journey. Whatever the case, I think you're brave, and I believe your commitment to take the hard but necessary steps to healing is going to pay off in the next few weeks.

You may be wondering if it is necessary to read the corresponding book, *Is it Me? Making Sense of Your Confusing Marriage,* in order to experience the healing from this workbook. The answer is YES. This workbook is not a substitute for the book. It actually takes the information you learn from each chapter in the book and, through the use of specially crafted writing and processing exercises, helps you pull all the material together in a way that challenges your core beliefs and addresses the trauma so you can get on with a full and meaningful life.

This workbook is not a sweet, fluffy piece of candy that melts in your mouth and slips down your throat with a sigh of pleasure. Instead, it's more like a surgical scalpel that will cut deep to the core of who you are and what you've experienced, and it's going to hurt like crazy. But it will bring you deep healing and hope for a better future, and there are warm blankets of comfort laid out for you here and there along the way.

You are going to take the manure the enemy put into your life, and you're going to make fertilizer. Fertilizer that will nourish the soil of your future and feed your new life. The power behind this miracle is the power of the Living God. Your Creator. This is His specialty!

"For I am about to do something new. See, I have already begun! Do you not see it? I will make a pathway through the wilderness. I will create rivers in the dry wasteland." Isaiah 43:19

Because we are doing surgery here, you may get triggered. If that happens, you may need to take a break and ground yourself. Stop what you're doing and take slow, deep breaths. Listen, concentrating on the sounds around you. Look, concentrating on the details of the things you see. Feel, concentrating on the temperature of the air or the feel of the blanket on your legs. Smell, concentrating on the scents around you. Taste, concentrating on the tea you're drinking.

Once you've grounded yourself, you may begin again. If you're unable to ground yourself, leave the work behind and try again another time. Or if you have a person you can trust, ask her or a therapist to work through this material with you. This can be slow work. Be patient with yourself.

You won't see specific days or time frames assigned to each page. YOU get to decide what pace you want to take. Some days you may want to work hard. Other days you will be exhausted and unable to think clearly to do any work. I suggest making yourself a small goal each week to get a certain amount done, but you'll want to hold that goal loosely so you can be gentle with your needs. You can take one week, two weeks, or however many weeks **you need** to do Week One, Week Two, Week Three, and so forth. You are a precious treasure. Advocate for yourself and protect yourself. This pleases your Creator.

Everyone who goes through this workbook will be in a different place on their journey. You may be just waking up to the abuse in your life, or you may be separated or in the process of a divorce. Perhaps you've been divorced for a long time, and you are just now addressing some of the things you went through in your previous marriage so you can heal and move on.

Depending on where you are, some of the exercises may or may not apply to you. You may need to look at things in retrospect to get a sense of break-through and healing. That's okay. If something doesn't apply, just skip it. Or change it in whatever way works best for your situation. This workbook is meant to help **you**. So you get to do with it whatever you feel is best right now. (You may find it helpful to go through it again in one year to see how much progress you've made!)

Using This Workbook in a Small Group

Some women will use this book in the privacy of their homes, interacting with the material on their own. Others may use it as part of a small group study either locally or online. There are group discussion questions at the end of each chapter to facilitate healthy conversations around the material. If you do this in a group, I recommend breaking down into groups of three and giving each participant five minutes to share per question. (SET A TIMER! This makes it objective and fair to each person in the group.) Doing it this way would take one hour. If the group wanted to go for two hours, you could have six participants per group each sharing for five minutes per question, OR you could stick to three participants per group and give them each ten minutes to share per question. Discuss the needs of the group together and decide what works best for your particular group.

Other Tips for Using This Workbook

While going through this workbook, you may be asked to imagine things that are not part of your current reality. In fact, they may never be a reality for you. You might wonder, "What's the point of that?" The goal behind this is to wake up parts of your brain and rational reasoning skills so you can see the unhealthy beliefs, relationships, and areas of your life you've accepted as normal and okay. Once you can identify those areas, you will naturally begin to take small steps to change them. But it starts with recognizing them in the first place. (And you would be surprised at how shifts in our thinking and beliefs actually create shifts in the course of our life as well. You may find many things you can only imagine now will actually come true for you later on in life!)

Beliefs are like seeds. They start small and hidden, but over time they grow into huge oak trees. If you've got some oak-tree beliefs in your life, you can't just replace those trees with new belief seeds and expect to see brand new trees overnight. But ten years from now? Yes! You'll see tremendous growth come from those seeds. Ten years is coming whether you plant new seeds today or not. Ten years from now you'll either have a bigger, older oak tree, or you'll have a solid, younger one that is flourishing. ***Your work here is seed planting.*** It might not feel worth it some days, but ten years from now, you'll be glad you did.

Finally, I'd like to leave you with this. As a woman living in a destructive relationship, you have no control over many things in your life. There is a sense of hopelessness and despair that comes with that reality. But you need to know that even though you have no control over many, perhaps even most things in your life, you do have control over your inner world. Nobody can touch that but you and God. So carefully guard and protect that sacred space, and use this book and workbook to expand that space, breathing new oxygen, love, and life into your inner world—life that will strengthen and empower you to be whole and healthy.

Fly Free,

Natalie Hoffman

September, 2019

Week One

IS THIS YOUR MARRIAGE?

"So often survivors have had their experiences denied, trivialized, or distorted. Writing is an important avenue for healing because it gives you the opportunity to define your own reality. You can say: This did happen to me. It was that bad. It was the fault & responsibility of the adult. I was—and am—innocent."

THE COURAGE TO HEAL BY ELLEN BASS & LAURA DAVIS

"He was despised and rejected—a man of sorrows, acquainted with deepest grief. We turned our backs on him and looked the other way. He was despised, and we did not care."

ISAIAH 53:3 (NLT)

"Even if my father and mother abandon me, the LORD will hold me close."

PSALM 27:10 (NLT)

READING ASSIGNMENT

Chapter One: Is This Your Marriage?

SUMMARY POINTS

1. In an emotionally abusive marriage, your partner's behavior hurts and confuses you, and he doesn't take personal responsibility for that behavior but rather denies, justifies, and minimizes his behavior while placing the blame on you or some other outside force.

2. An abusive partner's behavior is chronic and doesn't get better with time.

3. Emotional abuse is the most prevalent type of abuse in Christian communities.

4. Hidden emotional domestic abuse is secret, regular, and repeated cruel mistreatment of the inner emotions and heart of another person living within the same home.

5. Some abusers only use covert tactics, making it even more difficult to recognize it as abuse and get help for it.

6. The one common denominator of emotional abusers is that they are unable to take responsibility for their behavior. You can't solve marriage problems with someone who will not take responsibility or be held accountable for their destructive behavior.

7. It takes two people to make a relationship work. It only takes one to destroy it and cause harm to the other person in the relationship.

WHEN YOU ARE FINISHED WITH WORKBOOK CHAPTER ONE YOU WILL:

•   Have a clearer understanding of what is going on in your marriage.

•   Catch a glimpse of how your marriage has affected who you are as a person.

•   Understand the definition of covert emotional abuse and how it's showing up in your marriage.

•   Begin to identify patterns in your interactions with your partner.

•   Recognize different ways you've tried to fix things over the years without seeing measurable results.

MINING FOR GOLD

1. What was the golden nugget you found in chapter one? Write down a favorite quote or new idea.

_____

_____

_____

_____

2. What did you believe before you read this chapter?

_____

_____

_____

_____

3. How were your prior beliefs challenged in this chapter?

_____

_____

_____

_____

4. How will the golden nugget you discovered help your life look different ten years from now?

_____

_____

_____

_____

HOW YOU VIEW YOURSELF

Below are some words to describe different attributes people have or different ways they may feel about themselves. You may want to select two different pen colors to complete this exercise. **CIRCLE the words that describe how you perceived yourself BEFORE you got married. UNDERLINE the words that best fit how you perceive yourself now that you've been married for several years.**

Encouraged	Original	Candid	Creative
Empathic	Hardworking	Optimistic	Adventurous
Sad	Controlling	Desperate	Stupid
Anxious	Lost	Insecure	Hesitant
Leader	Cooperative	Persistent	Clever
Secure	Unselfish	Team Player	Hopeful
Confused	Passive	Boring	Lonely
Worthless	Hopeless	Apathetic	Indecisive
Initiator	Independent	Motivated	Innovative
Upbeat	Self-Disciplined	Gentle	Peaceful
Miserable	Negative	Ugly	Exhausted
Angry	Unmotivated	Distant	Weak
Patient	Cheerful	Imaginative	Loyal
Articulate	Strong	Respectful	Achiever
Shy	Discouraged	Trapped	Sickly
Fearful	Depressed	Watchful	Enabling

What additional words would you use to describe who you were and what you were like BEFORE you were married? _____

_____

_____

What additional words would you use to describe who you were and what you were like AFTER you were married? _____

_____

_____

PATTERNS OF BEHAVIOR

Here is a list of patterns of behavior found in chapter one. Which of these patterns of behavior do you see in your marriage?

☐ Is your partner chronically dishonest? Does he leave out information with the intent to mislead or hide something from you? Does he say things happened that didn't? Likewise, does he say things didn't happen that did?

☐ Does he chronically say he will do something, but he doesn't always follow through on those commitments?

☐ Does he chronically inflate his own good deeds while minimizing your efforts? Does he point out to you what he's done and expect praise for normal adult responsibilities?

☐ Does he chronically criticize your efforts and shame you for your preferences?

☐ Does he chronically turn a discussion into an argument and blame you for intentionally starting that argument?

☐ Does he chronically ignore your efforts to connect? Does he delay answering emails or texts or phone calls? Does he avoid eye contact when you are talking to him? Does he sigh or scoff and use facial and body language that indicate his disinterest and annoyance toward you?

☐ Does he chronically blame you for the things he himself needs to take responsibility for? Are you his scapegoat?

☐ Does he chronically put his own needs, wants, or interests above yours?

☐ Does he chronically interpret the slightest disagreement with his decisions, opinions, or desires to be disrespectful on your part? Does he claim that, because you don't "respect" him by agreeing with him, that you are failing as a wife? Does he demand respect regardless of his behavior?

☐ Is he chronically critical of your interests, hobbies, choice of clothing, personal style, friendships, fears, hopes, and dreams?

☐ Is he chronically sullen when you are happy, and, alternatively, is he is happy-go-lucky when you are suffering in some way?

☐ Is he chronically unavailable when you need him most, such as during pregnancy or following the birth of a baby or the death of a family member or friend?

☐ Is he chronically uninvolved in the daily routine of raising the family and running the household? Does he show up only when he feels like it or when it suits his timetable or agenda or when someone from the outside is observing him, such as at church or an extended family gathering?

☐ Does he chronically project his own poor attitudes and behavior onto you, accusing you of feeling and doing the very things he himself feels and does?

☐ Does he chronically tell you what you are thinking? Does he presume to interpret your heart and motives? Does he maintain that his accusations of you are true regardless of what you've explained?

☐ Does he chronically use you in bed, meeting his own needs while disregarding yours? Has he ever forced you to have sex when you didn't want to?

☐ Does he chronically lay the blame for the marriage problems on your shoulders? Is he unable to take responsibility for his behavior? Is he offended when you give him feedback about those behaviors?

☐ Does he chronically create an environment in which he does everything right while you do very little right? Does he withhold praise and encouragement and instead belittle you and makes you feel small and insignificant?

☐ Does he chronically control the money and/or other assets?

☐ Does he chronically control what you do with your time? Does he demand your time and attention when you are giving it to others, even in serious times like family deaths? Does he attempt to isolate you?

☐ Does he chronically control other aspects of your life together without regard to your input, needs, or desires? Some examples might be how you decorate the home, what food you eat, how many children you have, child rearing policies, etc.

☐ Does he chronically disrespect your boundaries? Are you allowed to say "stop" or "no" without suffering emotional and verbal consequences?

☐ Does he chronically sabotage your emotions before bed, an important commitment with others, or a special event? Does he shame you or try to upset you in public?

☐ Does he chronically withhold communication and affection in order to control your emotions and decisions? Does he withdraw for hours or days, punishing you with a silent treatment?

☐ Does he chronically refuse to take responsibility for his actions and attitudes in your relationship by blame-shifting, denying, justifying, and minimizing his behaviors?

☐ Does he chronically sweep conflict under the rug, never to be resolved?

☐ Does he chronically punish you later for something he's agreed about or praised you about earlier? Does he frequently change his positive judgments of you into negative ones later on?

☐ Has he made it clear to you that certain topics are off limits?

☐ Does he chronically accuse you of trying to control him? Does he accuse you of having the motives or behavior patterns that he does?

☐ **Is trying to solve your partner's problems and manage his emotions all you can think about?** Do these problems steal your attention from everything and everyone, including God, so that your focus is constantly on them? **Is solving the confusion in your marriage the center of your painful world?**

Does he ever:

☐ Accuse you of something to get the focus off his behavior?

☐ Blame you for his behavior?

☐ Block the discussion?

☐ Withhold information to keep you in the dark?

☐ Correct the things you say in order to create confusion and doubt?

☐ Discount your credibility?

☐ Scoff at your concerns?

☐ Judge and criticize you?

☐ Threaten you?

☐ Call you names?

☐ Intimidate you?

☐ Minimize the impact of his behavior?

☐ Tell you that you're making a mountain out of a molehill or creating drama?

☐ Accuse you of not trusting God?

☐ Deny his behavior?

☐ Justify his behavior?

Are there any other destructive chronic behaviors not listed here that are showing up in your relationship?

_____

_____

_____

If one of your closest friends checked off the same number of boxes you did, would you believe she was in an emotionally destructive relationship? What would you tell her? _____

_____

_____

_____

DOMESTIC COVERT EMOTIONAL ABUSE

All abuse is about power and control. The patterns of behavior we've just looked at describe an emotionally abusive relationship. This isn't just a difficult marriage relationship. It isn't just a challenging marriage relationship. It isn't just a confusing marriage relationship. It's an abusive marriage relationship. I believe emotional abuse is the most common, most destructive, and most dehumanizing type of intimate partner abuse. And because of the covert tactics employed in such a relationship, it is the most difficult type of abuse to identify. My definition of hidden emotional domestic abuse *is the secret, regular, and repeated cruel mistreatment of the inner emotions and heart of another person living within the same home.*

SECRET: How has your experience been kept hidden from the rest of the people in your life?

_____

_____

_____

REGULAR AND REPEATED: How has your experience been regular and repeated throughout your marriage?

_____

_____

_____

CRUEL MISTREATMENT: Think of a young girl you know like a daughter or niece. If that girl were to experience the things you have experienced, what would you tell her about her experience? Would you tell her it was appropriate and healthy or cruel and unhealthy? Explain why.

_____

_____

_____

EMOTIONS AND HEART: How has your husband's behavior impacted your emotional, physical, spiritual, and mental well-being?

Emotional: _____

_____

_____

Physical: _____

_____

_____

Spiritual: _____

_____

_____

Mental: _____

_____

_____

ANOTHER PERSON: How do you view yourself? Do you see yourself as an extension of your husband's life or as a separate person with just as much value and worth as anyone else? How do you think he views you?

_____

_____

_____

IN YOUR HOME: Home should be a safe haven full of love, warmth, peace, and joy. How has the abuse in your home created chronic problems for you? What are some of those problems?

_____

_____

_____

Journal Exercise

Processing an Event

Think of an incident that happened recently in which you and your husband had an altercation that left you feeling confused and in emotional pain.

What happened first? _____

_____

What triggered the problem? _____

_____

How did the conversation go? What did he say and how did he say it? What did you say and how did you say it? _____

_____

_____

How did the conversation make you feel? _____

_____

How did it get resolved or not resolved? _____

What are some of patterns of behavior you notice in this incident?

HIS TYPICAL BEHAVIOR PATTERNS:_____

_____

YOUR TYPICAL BEHAVIOR PATTERNS: _____

_____

How does this incident represent your overall relationship with your husband? _____

_____

_____

_____

Using your imagination, rewrite what would happen in the situation if your husband took responsibility for his behavior, made amends, and changed his behavior. _____

_____

_____

_____

In your new story, how did your character feel about and respond to your husband's new behavior? _____

_____

_____

_____

If the past is the best predictor of the future, how realistic is it that this new story could become a reality for you one day? Why or why not? _____

_____

_____

_____

If you could go back in time, is there anything about your behavior or response to your husband that you would change? If so, what was it? _____

_____

_____

_____

How do you think your husband would respond to your new behavior? The same? Better? Worse? Describe what you think would happen. _____

_____

_____

_____

How would **_you_** feel differently about the incident if you had done things differently? _____

_____

_____

_____

Brainstorm all the things you've tried to do over the years to fix your particular marriage. Next to each thing, describe how your partner responded to it. Did it work? Why or why not?

1. _____

_____

2. _____

_____

3. _____

_____

4. _____

_____

5. _____

_____

PRAYER

"The Lord is a refuge for the oppressed, a stronghold in times of trouble."—Psalm 9:9

Dear Heavenly Father,

I feel overwhelmed by the seriousness of what I'm dealing with here. I've always known something was horribly wrong, but how can I call this abuse? That seems like such a heavy word. Is it really true? I don't want it to be true. I want to wake up and have this all be a bad dream. I don't like my life, but pretending feels more comfortable. Waking up feels terrifying.

I don't know what to do. And even if I did, I don't know how I'd do it. I don't feel very strong. I'm confused.

But… YOU know exactly what is going on in my life. You are intimately acquainted with the details of my relationship with my husband. When we have crazy conversations that I can't follow, YOU keep track of every word. YOU know the truth, and You are not confused in the least.

Did you lead me to this book? To this study? Please help me. Please show me the truth. I don't know if I am ready, but I'm going to try. I will open my eyes and trust that You will lead and guide me in the way You'd have me to go. I only want to follow You and bring glory to You with my life. But I'm not sure how to do that in this marriage.

I feel so helpless and hopeless. I feel like a trapped animal in a corner. One minute I want to hide, and the next minute I feel ready to fight. But I don't want this for my life! I want peace. I want inner rest. I want real joy.

I want to be free from this corner. I want to be free from the poisonous air I breathe. I remember who I was many years ago, and I want to find that girl and bring her back to life again.

Help me. Help me. Help me. I don't know how You will. I only know that I can ask, and so I do. I ask You to help me.

In Jesus Name,

Amen

GROUP DISCUSSION QUESTIONS

1. How did you relate to this first chapter? Could you see your marriage described here? In what ways?

_____

_____

_____

_____

2. Did you have a light bulb moment? If so, what was it?

_____

_____

_____

_____

3. How do you feel after reading this chapter, and why do you think you feel that way?

_____

_____

_____

_____

4. What is one way your life will be different after reading this chapter?

_____

_____

_____

_____

Week Two

WHAT DOES A
NORMAL MARRIAGE LOOK LIKE?

"In a healthy relationship, vulnerability is wonderful. It leads to increased intimacy and closer bonds. When a healthy person realizes that he or she hurt you, they feel remorse and they make amends. It's safe to be honest. In an abusive system, vulnerability is dangerous. It's considered a weakness, which acts as an invitation for more mistreatment. Abusive people feel a surge of power when they discover a weakness. They exploit it, using it to gain more power. Crying or complaining confirms that they've poked you in the right spot."

THE RESCUED SOUL:
THE WRITING JOURNEY FOR THE HEALING OF INCEST AND FAMILY BETRAYAL
BY CHRISTINA ENEVOLDSEN

"If I have the gift of prophecy and can fathom all mysteries and all knowledge, and if I have a faith that can move mountains, but do not have love, I am nothing."

1 CORINTHIANS 13:2

"Be devoted to one another in love. Honor one another above yourselves."

ROMANS 12:10

READING ASSIGNMENT

Chapter Two: What Does a Normal Marriage Look Like?

SUMMARY POINTS:

1. A normal marriage is not confusing.

2. Mutuality is the bedrock of a Christian marriage.

3. A normal marriage has mutual love.

4. A normal marriage has mutual respect.

5. A normal marriage has mutual honesty.

6. A normal marriage has mutual vulnerability

7. A normal marriage has mutual responsibility.

8. A normal marriage has mutual submission.

WHEN YOU ARE FINISHED WITH WORKBOOK CHAPTER TWO YOU WILL:

• Be able to determine whether or not your marriage is normal.

• Know what mutuality is and be able to discern if your relationship is a mutual one or not.

• Have analyzed whether or not mutual love, mutual respect, mutual honesty, mutual vulnerability, mutual responsibility, and mutual submission are being played out in your relationship.

MINING FOR GOLD

1. What was the golden nugget you found in chapter two? Write down a favorite quote or new idea.

_____

_____

_____

_____

2. What did you believe before you read this chapter?

_____

_____

_____

_____

3. How were your prior beliefs challenged in this chapter?

_____

_____

_____

_____

4. How will the golden nugget you discovered help your life look different ten years from now?

_____

_____

_____

_____

IS MY MARRIAGE NORMAL? EXERCISE

Circle "yes" or "no" to the following statements to determine if your marriage is normal or not according to the definitions in chapter two. Try not to analyze the questions. Just give your initial, knee jerk answer. Let your gut speak!

1. YES NO When I think about my relationship with my partner, I am at peace.
2. YES NO My partner and I work together as a team.
3. YES NO My partner and I make decisions together.
4. YES NO My partner and I are able to compromise peacefully most of the time.
5. YES NO Neither one of us holds all the power in our relationship. We share power.
6. YES NO We are devoted to one another in love. My partner would never throw me under the bus.
7. YES NO We are both faithful to one another sexually. This includes no use of porn.
8. YES NO We both take responsibility for our behavior on bad days and say we're sorry.
9. YES NO Neither one of us accuses or blames the other one for something we've done.
10. YES NO We are able to give each other feedback without worrying about making the other one angry.
11. YES NO We are both open to feedback because we want to know how we can love the other one better.
12. YES NO I respect my partner, and he respects me.
13. YES NO We both support and encourage our partner to use his/her gifts and talents.
14. YES NO We both pay attention when the other one is talking or sharing something.
15. YES NO We admire one another and are proud of the other one's work and life.
16. YES NO We completely trust one another.
17. YES NO I never have to worry that I'm not getting the whole story.
18. YES NO My partner acknowledges my emotions and reality as important.
19. YES NO I am totally safe with my partner.
20. YES NO I feel comfortable with who I am when I'm with my partner in bed.
21. YES NO My partner is open and honest with me about his inner world and vice versa.
22. YES NO My partner and I lovingly submit to one another out of reverence for Jesus.
23. YES NO My partner and I respect one another even if we disagree on things.
24. YES NO When we disagree about a decision, sometimes I defer to my partner, and sometimes my partner defers to me.
25. YES NO When I share something hard that I'm going through, my partner listens with compassion and empathy and vice versa.

Now that you've completed this exercise, describe your marriage using the first ten words that come to the top of your head. Circle the three that describe your marriage the best.

1. _____   6. _____

2. _____   7. _____

3. _____   8. _____

4. _____   9. _____

5. _____   10. _____

All healthy relationships are governed by the law of love. This means if your marriage is not usually reflecting mutual love, joy, peace, patience, kindness, goodness, gentleness, and self-control, it's not a healthy marriage, let alone a Christian one. These characteristics of the evidence of the Holy Spirit at work in two people go both ways, not one way. Understanding the necessity of mutuality is critical to understanding why your marriage is destructive. It isn't because you haven't tried hard enough. It's because your relationship isn't mutual. Mutuality is the key.

Describe what you believe a mutual marriage would look like. _____

_____

_____

_____

_____

How does your marriage compare/contrast with your description? _____

_____

_____

_____

_____

MUTUAL LOVE

What are the ways you're working hard to love your partner and why? _____

_____

_____

_____

What are the ways your partner is working hard to love you? If he's not, what are the ways he is showing you a lack of love? What are your typical ways of responding to that? _____

_____

_____

_____

MUTUAL HONESTY

Do you trust your husband? Why or why not? _____

_____

_____

_____

What are the typical ways you respond to your husband when you are unable to trust something he says or does? Why do you think you respond in those ways? _____

_____

_____

_____

MUTUAL VULNERABILITY

We increase our vulnerability with one another when we can show up fully ourselves and be totally safe. We know the other person will not take advantage of our vulnerability.

What are some ways you've made yourself vulnerable in your marriage? _____

_____

_____

_____

_____

_____

How has your partner responded to your vulnerability? _____

_____

_____

_____

_____

_____

How has your husband made himself vulnerable in his relationship with you? _____

_____

_____

_____

_____

_____

MUTUAL RESPONSIBILITY

List the various ways you are taking responsibility (owning your own behaviors) in your relationship.

_____

_____

_____

_____

_____

List the various ways your partner is taking responsibility (owning his own behaviors) in the relationship.

_____

_____

_____

_____

_____

After looking at your answers above, do you feel you both work to take equal responsibility for making your relationship successful? If not, why not?

_____

_____

_____

_____

_____

MUTUAL SUBMISSION

Submission is a voluntary attitude of respect and cooperation, and it's critical when it comes to quality relationships. The definition of abuse is when one person takes power and control over another person.

According to the scope of what the Bible teaches about human relationships, who is supposed to submit in a Christian relationship? _____

_____

_____

_____

_____

_____

Do you believe it is healthy for one adult to have power over another adult in an intimate marriage relationship? Why or why not? _____

_____

_____

_____

_____

_____

Would you describe your marriage as mutually submissive? Why or why not? Is there one partner who has power and control over the other one? In what ways? _____

_____

_____

_____

_____

_____

WRITE YOUR OWN PRAYER

"The LORD himself goes before you and will be with you; he will never leave you nor forsake you. Do not be afraid; do not be discouraged."—Deuteronomy 31:8

Dear Heavenly Father,

I'm realizing that: _____

_____

_____

_____

I feel: _____

_____

_____

_____

Help me with: _____

_____

_____

_____

I want to give You: _____

_____

_____

_____

GROUP DISCUSSION QUESTIONS

1. Do you believe a wife should expect reciprocity in her marriage relationship? Why or why not?

_____

_____

_____

_____

2. Would you describe your marriage as normal? Why or why not? If not, when did you start to wonder if it wasn't normal? What helped you wake up to start seeing the reality of your situation?

_____

_____

_____

_____

3. What is one thing you've accepted as "normal" in your marriage that you now realize isn't?

_____

_____

_____

_____

4. Pick one of the following and talk about how NOT having mutuality in that area has hurt your marriage: love (opposite: hate or indifference), respect (opposite: disregard, scorn, disdain), responsibility (opposite: apathetic, irresponsible, blame shifter), honesty (opposite: dishonest, withholding information, untrustworthy), vulnerability (opposite: arrogant, has to be right), and submission (opposite: controlling).

_____

_____

_____

_____

THE PROPAGANDA MACHINE

"If you can convince people that freedom is injustice, they will then believe that slavery is freedom."

STEFAN MOLYNEUX – A MODERN DAY WHITE SUPREMACIST

"It is for freedom that Christ has set us free. Stand firm, then, and do not let yourselves be burdened again by a yoke of slavery."

GALATIANS 5:1

"The Spirit of the Sovereign LORD is on me, because the LORD has anointed me to proclaim good news to the poor. He has sent me to bind up the brokenhearted, to proclaim freedom for the captives and release from darkness for the prisoners."

ISAIAH 61:1

READING ASSIGNMENT

Chapter Three: The Propaganda Machine

SUMMARY POINTS:

1. Propaganda is biased information spread within a closed group in order to influence the group to believe or behave in specific ways. Propaganda is a way of slipping bad thoughts and ideas into the collective consciousness of a group of people by presenting those thoughts and ideas as appealing and good and right.

2. Much of the organized conservative church uses the Bible to establish their own biased ideas and stereotypes about men and women in order to control women and perpetuate abuse.

3. Good words can hide evil intentions. Just because someone is using God's words doesn't mean they speak for God.

4. There are a handful of verses used to promote a power-over theology of women; however, the entire scope of the Bible and its themes promote equality, unity, and oneness among humanity regardless of gender, race, or socioeconomic status.

5. Hierarchy defines the world's dysfunctional, power-grabbing system, but hierarchy is not part of God's kingdom.

6. An abusive marriage tells a lie about God.

WHEN YOU ARE FINISHED WITH WORKBOOK CHAPTER THREE YOU WILL:

*   See how religious propaganda has affected your life.

*   Understand what the Bible teaches about mutuality vs. power-over.

*   Recognize how hierarchy plays a key role in abusive relationships.

*   Practice rewiring lies you have believed for many years.

MINING FOR GOLD

1. What was the golden nugget you found in chapter three? Write down a favorite quote or new idea.

_____

_____

_____

_____

2. What did you believe before you read this chapter?

_____

_____

_____

_____

3. How were your prior beliefs challenged in this chapter?

_____

_____

_____

_____

4. How will the golden nugget you discovered help your life look different ten years from now?

_____

_____

_____

_____

WHAT HAVE YOU BELIEVED?

The following statements are found in chapter three. Put a check mark by the statements you believe now or have believed in the past.

☐ "I believed I was making him unhappy, and if I could just fix things, he would go back to being the kind man I met."

☐ "I believed if I tried harder, if I sacrificed more, gave more, loved more, I would measure up, and we would have peace and harmony."

☐ "I believed I had made a vow before God, and I had to make it work even if he wasn't keeping his vow."

☐ "I believed if I suffered enough, it might finally be enough to change him."

☐ "I believed it was God's will for me to suffer."

☐ "I believed that I had no right to express hurt over my husband's abuse because I wasn't perfect and also sinned."

☐ "I believed I was not worthy of honor."

☐ "I believed suffering was godly, and God approved when I pretended it wasn't happening. Overlooking sin was my Christian duty."

☐ "I believed to obey my husband was to obey God. They were equivalent."

☐ "I believed that God could change him if I just prayed hard enough and gave it enough time."

☐ "I believed I would be a failure if I gave up on the marriage."

☐ "I believed if my husband was unhappy with me and my performance, God was unhappy with me too."

☐ "I believed he had potential, and I was going to be the person who made the difference in his life."

☐ "I believed I needed to keep his cruelty toward me under wraps or I'd be disrespecting my husband."

☐ "I believed if I was more fun, sexier, prettier, and skinnier, he would love me."

☐ "I believed my faith was responsible for his heart and behavior. If he was being abusive, I must not have enough faith."

☐ "I believed I needed to be prepared to die at the hands of my spouse if need be. This was my Christian duty."

☐ "I believed I needed to forgive even though he was never sorry, and I must never bring up how much it hurt."

☐ "I believed all our marriage problems were my fault in one way or another."

☐ "I believed nobody would believe me."

- ☐ "I believed I would lose my church, my family, my friends, and my emotional and spiritual support if I told the truth about what was happening to me."

- ☐ "I believed if I left, God wouldn't love me anymore."

- ☐ "I believed every desire should be fulfilled in Christ alone, and it was wrong for me to expect love and kindness from my partner."

- ☐ "I believed I made my bed, and now I had to lie in it. No way out."

- ☐ "I believed the millions of painful incidents were not enough to warrant leaving. I could only leave if he did something huge, like beat me up. I used to pray he would."

About Women

- ☐ Women are emotional and therefore tend to make rash decisions.

- ☐ Women don't want sex as much as men do.

- ☐ Women need love, but respect is for the men.

- ☐ Women are to submit to their husbands no matter what.

- ☐ Women belong to their fathers until marriage, and then they belong to their husbands.

- ☐ Women are created to be keepers of the home. If a woman pursues a career outside of the home, she is disobeying God.

- ☐ Women are one-down from men—second in command.

- ☐ Women must like female colors, wear skirts, and have long hair.

- ☐ Women stumble men with their bodies, therefore they must keep themselves covered up. How covered up depends on the church you go to.

- ☐ Women who have opinions that differ from the men in their lives are rebellious.

- ☐ Women who bring up a problem are like a dripping faucet.

- ☐ Women can work in the church nursery, but they cannot teach a man.

- ☐ Women are subordinate to men.

- ☐ Women should not be in leadership positions.

- ☐ Women aren't allowed to have boundaries.

- ☐ Good women cooperate, accept, smile, and submit sweetly and quietly. Bad women point out problems and make trouble.

- ☐ Good women please their husbands and obey them like children obey their mommies and daddies.

- ☐ Good women don't try to learn more than their husbands do about theology. Being educated and well-read will only make their husbands feel inferior.

About Men

☐ Men are rational and logical and by their very nature make good leaders.

☐ Men are created to be heads of state, heads of the church, and heads of their homes.

☐ Men require respect.

☐ Men need sex—lots of it. It is their right to have it.

☐ Men aren't natural nurturers and shouldn't be expected to be nurturing. That's weak, and men should be strong in every way.

☐ Men should oversee and be responsible for what their wives do at home and how they parent the children.

☐ Men require obedience and submission in order to feel respected and motivated to do their manly things.

☐ Men are required by God to make sure their wives and children submit to God by submitting to him as their head.

☐ Men need to make sure their wives aren't getting too uppity and knowledgeable. They might become rebellious.

☐ Men make better decisions, but when they feel it is appropriate, they can get help from their wives as long as she understands that his word is final.

☐ Men are qualified to teach anyone by virtue of their manhood.

☐ Men have more important things to do than babysit their kids and contribute to the housework. They have KINGDOM work, after all.

☐ Men must not show weakness. To acknowledge mistakes or sin is weakness and will bring down a man's ego and destroy him.

☐ When a husband and wife come to an impasse, the husband gets the final say because he is God's anointed head of the home.

Pick one or two of the items you checked that you no longer believe. Why don't you believe those things any longer? What do you believe instead? _____

_____

_____

_____

_____

STUDY QUESTIONS

1. How have you seen misogyny (prejudice toward women) show up in your religious circles?

   _____

   _____

   _____

2. *"Closed groups form their own set of beliefs and often discourage members of the group from reading and learning outside of their group's own set of books, classes, schools, and favored news stations."* Have you experienced this? How?

   _____

   _____

   _____

3. Do you believe deeply rooted beliefs and stereotypes about women could be the reason our culture and the conservative church refuse to address and correct abuse? What are some ways others have viewed you as a woman throughout your life that have hindered your emotional, physical, and spiritual health and growth? Whose negative view of you damaged you? A pastor, mother, father, sibling, teacher, doctor, or...?

   _____

   _____

   _____

4. What did you learn in chapter three about God's view of hierarchy (power-over) in the Bible? How do you feel right now about what you've learned?

   _____

   _____

   _____

5. How has hierarchy (power-over) played a role in your marriage?

   _____

   _____

   _____

Journal Brain Rewiring Exercise

Replacing Lies with the Truth

1. Think of a recent experience in which you believed something negative about yourself as a woman. Write down what you believed about yourself. (You can pick one of the statements you checked in the earlier exercise if you'd like.)

    _____

    _____

    _____

    _____

2. What did the different parts of your body feel when you believed that thing about yourself? What did your stomach feel? Your head? Your shoulders? Your back? Your chest?

    _____

    _____

    _____

    _____

3. Describe your emotions when you were believing that thing. Were you anxious? Angry? Hopeless? Lonely? Fearful? Empty? Numb?

    _____

    _____

    _____

    _____

4. Look at your belief and rewrite it so it says the OPPOSITE of what it says now. For example, if you wrote: "I believed I had no right to express pain about what my husband did to me because I was also imperfect and a sinner." You would re-write it like this: "I do have a right to express pain about what my husband does to me because I am human and have feelings and needs that are just as important as anyone else's."

Pick three of the "I believe" statements in the earlier exercise that most resonate with you, and rewrite them to communicate the OPPOSITE message. Imagine that you are helping that woman rewire her own brain with the truth. I will do another one for you:

I believed...if I left, God wouldn't love me anymore.

The truth is...I believe God's love for me is based on His goodness and faithfulness, and not based on anything I can or can't do. I believe God will love me whether I stay or leave. He has already suffered on my behalf, and His sacrifice sets me free.

Your turn:

1. I believed... _____

   _____

   _____

   The truth is... _____

   _____

   _____

2. I believed... _____

   _____

   _____

   The truth is.... _____

   _____

   _____

3. I believed... _____

   _____

   _____

   The truth is... _____

   _____

   _____

PRAYER

"There is no longer Jew or Gentile, slave or free, male and female. For you are all one in Christ Jesus."—Galatians 3:28 (NLT)

But Jesus called them together and said, "You know that the rulers in this world lord it over their people, and officials flaunt their authority over those under them. But among you it will be different. Whoever wants to be a leader among you must be your servant, and whoever wants to be first among you must become your slave. For even the Son of Man came not to be served but to serve others and to give his life as a ransom for many."—Matthew 20:25-28 (NLT)

"The one who speaks on his own authority seeks his own glory; but the one who seeks the glory of him who sent him is true, and in him there is no falsehood."—John 7:18 (ESV)

Dear Abba Father,

Thank you that when you look at your sons and daughters, You are filled with love for all of us regardless of race or gender. You have the same purpose and vision for all of us: unity and oneness in Jesus. And You have equipped and gifted all of your children to spread the love of Jesus Christ to this world.

Thank you that Your ways are not man's ways. With man, it's about authority and power and control. With You, it is different. It's about serving and loving and honoring others. Your true children, filled with Your Spirit, will be marked by this difference. A difference that reflects Your highest wisdom.

Thank you for painting this beautiful picture of Your kingdom so we can tell the difference between what is from You and what is not from You. Thank you that Your Word, Jesus Christ, and the words that come to us from the Bible live out and lay out Your truth, so we no longer need to be confused.

It is so simple. We know our brothers and sisters by their love and efforts to create safe spaces of respect for one another. Anything less than that is not of You. Help us to live and breathe in this truth.

Help me to let go of what others believe and teach and look only to You for direction and truth. Help me to live authentically regardless of how others around me choose to live. Help me be willing to stand alone in Your truth, regardless of what others believe about You or me.

Thank you for loving me and teaching me and walking with me on this painful road. I will trust You.

In Jesus Name,

Amen

GROUP DISCUSSION QUESTIONS

1. What were some of the things you believed about yourself and your responsibility to your marriage as well as to God? Where was the first place you learned or were taught those things? Who taught them to you? How did others benefit from your believing those things?

_____

_____

_____

2. In what ways have you been harmed emotionally or spiritually by a theology that teaches men inherently have power over women? Were you surprised to learn that God desires mutuality instead of power-over not just for Christian relationships in general, but for husbands and wives in particular? Why or why not?

_____

_____

_____

3. What are some ways your beliefs have changed over time? What caused you to change those beliefs?

_____

_____

_____

4. What is one of the most hurtful things you currently believe about yourself? Have the others in the group re-phrase that belief to say the OPPOSITE of it to you. Have them write it down, say it out loud to you, and then give you the paper they wrote it on. Take that home and practice rewiring those new truths into your brain and heart over the course of the next few weeks.

_____

_____

_____

Week Four

HIS ROLE

"An abuser can seem emotionally needy. You can get caught in a trap of catering to him, trying to fill a bottomless pit. But he's not so much needy as entitled, so no matter how much you give him, it will never be enough. He will just keep coming up with more demands because he believes his needs are your responsibility, until you feel drained down to nothing."

LUNDY BANCROFT, WHY DOES HE DO THAT?
INSIDE THE MINDS OF ANGRY AND CONTROLLING MEN

"Those who hate you will be clothed with shame, and the tent of the wicked will be no more."

JOB 8:22 (ESV)

"Among my people are wicked men who lie in wait for victims like a hunter hiding in a blind. They continually set traps to catch people."

JEREMIAH 5:26 (NLT)

Reading Assignment

Chapter Four: His Role

Summary Points:

1. An abusive man exhibits five common types of behavior:

    a. Deception

    b. Denial of Responsibility

    c. Inability to Empathize

    d. Control

    e. Mind Invasion

2. His core beliefs about men and women, and especially his core beliefs about what he is entitled to from you, are what drive his attitudes and behaviors.

3. He can only change if he himself chooses to change, which is extremely rare since he fully sees himself as entitled to do what he does. He doesn't believe he has a problem, and nobody can fix a problem they don't believe exists.

4. His beliefs drive his behavior, and his behavior eventually brings serious consequences to his life. You are not the cause of those consequences. He is. Abusers ultimately destroy themselves.

5. Just because you value growth and change doesn't mean he does.

6. When his "change" is on his terms, it isn't real change.

When you are finished with workbook chapter four you will:

- See how five categories of abuse are showing up in your own relationship.

- Identify some of your partner's core beliefs and how they play a role in his behavior toward you.

- Begin to notice some of the consequences your partner experiences (or SHOULD experience) as a result of his abusive behavior.

- Be able to discern whether or not your partner is making the necessary changes.

MINING FOR GOLD

1. What was the golden nugget you found in chapter four? Write down a favorite quote or new idea.

_____

_____

_____

_____

2. What did you believe before you read this chapter?

_____

_____

_____

_____

3. How were your prior beliefs challenged in this chapter?

_____

_____

_____

_____

4. How will the golden nugget you discovered help your life look different ten years from now?

_____

_____

_____

_____

Five Categories of Typical Emotional and Spiritual Abuse

There are specific behavior patterns we see in men who are emotionally and spiritually abusive. Let's look at five categories of typical behavior and see if you have experienced any of these in your relationship.

1. Deception

There are different ways to deceive another person. Most often we think of the obvious kind: outright lying. But there are other, more subtle and just as destructive ways to deceive others.

1. Omitting information. When you ask your partner a question, does he ever give you partial or vague answers, leaving out pertinent information that might help you understand a situation better?

   Example: Wife "Where did you go?" Husband "I went to the gas station." Wife "But you were gone for an hour. What did you do there?" Husband "What is your problem? I went to the gas station. Get off my back. You're always so suspicious." This interaction is abusive because the husband is withholding information that would either expose him or set his wife at ease. He refuses to answer the question and blames his wife for her reaction to his deception.

   Can you think of a time when your partner did this to you? Describe the situation.

   _____

   _____

   _____

   _____

   _____

   _____

   _____

   _____

   _____

   _____

2. Another deceptive tactic is called gaslighting. This is when someone tells you that you really didn't hear or experience something you heard or experienced.

Example: Wife "Why did you say or do such and such?" Husband "I never said or did that. You're always making stuff up in your head." This is abusive crazy-making. You can't have a trusting relationship with someone who accuses you of making things up in your head just because they don't want to take responsibility for their words or actions.

Can you think of a time when your partner used the gaslighting tactic on you? Does he ever tell you that you've made something up? Does he deny your experience or your reality? Write about it.

_____

_____

_____

_____

_____

_____

_____

_____

_____

_____

_____

_____

_____

_____

_____

_____

_____

3. Sometimes they will twist the truth by hiding a little bit of lie in it to make it confusing and difficult to unravel. This is actually a favorite tactic of Satan in the Bible, so it isn't surprising that abusers are good at it.

   Example: Husband "God says we should forgive, so you have to forgive me or you are disobeying God." The truth is that we are to forgive, but the lie twisted up in that truth is that a woman who exercises boundaries and implements consequences for bad behavior isn't being forgiving.

   How does your partner twist the truth? Can you think of something twisted he likes to say to shame/blame/manipulate you into doing what he wants you to do?

   "Enemies disguise themselves with their lips, but in their hearts they harbor deceit. Though their speech is charming, do not believe them..."—Proverbs 26:24-25a

   What is God telling us through the wisdom of this verse in Proverbs, and how would you apply it to how your husband treats you?

   _____

   _____

   _____

   _____

   _____

   _____

   _____

   _____

   _____

   _____

   _____

   _____

2. DENIAL OF RESPONSIBILITY

Abusive individuals will not take personal responsibility for their behaviors. When confronted, in order to get the focus off themselves and their behavior they will employ one of the following tactics:

- **Deny it**   "I didn't do that."
- **Minimize it**   "It's not a big deal."
- **Justify it**   "I did it because _____."
- **Blame-shift**   "It's not my fault. It's your fault."

Can you think of examples in your relationship when your partner used these tactics? Write down an example of each tactic if you can.

Denial: _____

_____

Minimization: _____

_____

Justification: _____

_____

Blame-shifting: _____

_____

Are these responses typical of his behavior? YES   NO

"Whoever walks with the wise becomes wise, but the companion of fools will suffer harm."—Proverbs 13:20 (ESV)

How have you suffered harm as the companion of a fool?_____

_____

_____

_____

_____

_____

3. INABILITY TO EMPATHIZE

Empathy is the ability to put yourself in someone else's shoes in order to see an experience or belief from that other person's perspective. It's a necessary skill in order for two people to experience intimacy. Emotional abuse victims typically have a lot of empathy and assume their partner also has the same ability to empathize. Part of your healing will be to accept the fact that your partner does not have the ability to see life from anyone else's perspective. No matter how hard you try to help him with this, he will not be able to truly understand why you feel the way you do and how his behavior plays a major role in your destruction. At a core level he doesn't believe your personhood is valuable enough to "see" or understand.

Have you tried to explain how you feel about things without getting any understanding? Can you think of a situation where you worked hard to do this without getting anywhere? Describe it below.

_____

_____

_____

_____

How does it make you feel when your partner doesn't "see" you? _____

_____

_____

_____

"Behold, the eye of the Lord is on those who fear him, on those who hope in his steadfast love."—Psalm 33:18 (ESV)

"Even if my father and mother abandon me, the LORD will hold me close."—Psalm 27:10 (NLT)

What is God telling you through these verses? Do you believe Him? Why or why not?

_____

_____

_____

_____

_____

4. CONTROL

The very definition of abuse is that one person has control over another person. Some Christian circles teach that God wants men to control women—that God condones this kind of abuse. Nothing could be further from the truth. There are various kinds of control in abusive relationships. Let's look at three common ones. Which ones describe yours?

1. Financial control: does your partner control the finances? How? Are you required to support the family? Do you have freedom to make financial decisions?

   _____

   _____

   _____

   _____

2. Physical control: does your partner control any of the following either overtly or covertly? Where you go, what you wear, who you see, your schedule, where you work, what you make for dinner, etc.? Describe your experience, if any, with this kind of control:

   _____

   _____

   _____

   _____

3. Emotional control: does your partner play with your emotions? Does he try to push your buttons and then condemn you for your reactions? Does he accuse you of things you haven't done? Does he define your personhood, saying you are something you're not? Are you constantly confused about what is real and what isn't in your relationship? Do you experience frequent anxiety, anger, hopelessness, or sadness in your relationship? Describe your experience:

   _____

   _____

   _____

   _____

5. MIND INVASION

Over time, an emotional abuse victim will lose a healthy view of herself and begin to see herself through the eyes of her abusive partner. Since he views her as inferior and less-than, she will begin to feel that way about herself as well. This neutralizes her strength and personhood.

On a scale of 1-10, how would you rate your perception of yourself in the following areas? (A one would be "not at all" and a ten would be "absolutely YES!")

I have what it takes to be a good parent.	1 2 3 4 5 6 7 8 9 10
I make good decisions for myself and my family.	1 2 3 4 5 6 7 8 9 10
I like my body just the way it is, and I'm at home inside of it.	1 2 3 4 5 6 7 8 9 10
I have healthy boundaries, and I exercise them with confidence.	1 2 3 4 5 6 7 8 9 10
I don't have any problems saying "no" when I need to.	1 2 3 4 5 6 7 8 9 10
I can tolerate the disapproval of others who don't agree with me.	1 2 3 4 5 6 7 8 9 10
I can disagree with my partner, and we are still good with each other.	1 2 3 4 5 6 7 8 9 10
I feel like an adult who is in control of my own life.	1 2 3 4 5 6 7 8 9 10
I like my personality and my gifts.	1 2 3 4 5 6 7 8 9 10
I feel good about my ability to face the future.	1 2 3 4 5 6 7 8 9 10

Why do you think you rated yourself the way you did? What would you like to see different one year from now?_____

_____

_____

_____

_____

HIS CORE BELIEFS ABOUT HIMSELF

He believes he is above criticism and that any negative feedback about his behavior is exaggerated, unfounded, or ridiculous. Give an example of how this plays out in your relationship:

_____

_____

_____

_____

_____

He believes he is entitled to your body, your obedience, your respect, your subordination, and all the various aspects of your relationship. Give an example of how this plays out in your relationship.

_____

_____

_____

_____

_____

He believes he is a good man who does nothing wrong and will stop at nothing to convince others of this as well, even at his wife's expense. Give an example of how you've seen this play out in your relationship.

_____

_____

_____

_____

_____

HIS CORE BELIEFS ABOUT YOU AND YOUR MARRIAGE

Go back to chapter four and read about an emotional abuser's core beliefs about you.

What are five core beliefs your partner has about women and marriage? You can select from the suggestions given in chapter four, or you may have your own list. In the space below, write down the top five, along with an example for each belief. (PLEASE NOTE: His core beliefs are not what he SAYS he believes. They are what he SHOWS he believes by his behavior. Big difference!)

1. Core Belief: _____

_____

Example (how does he SHOW that he believes that): _____

_____

2. Core Belief: _____

_____

Example: _____

_____

3. Core Belief: _____

_____

Example: _____

_____

4. Core Belief: _____

_____

Example: _____

_____

5. Core Belief: _____

_____

Example: _____

_____

CONSEQUENCES OF HIS BEHAVIOR

"Whoever conceals his transgressions will not prosper, but he who confesses and forsakes them will obtain mercy."
—Proverbs 28:13 (ESV)

What does God say will happen to a person who refuses to take responsibility for his behavior?

_____

_____

_____

Have you seen this come true in your partner's life?   Yes   No

What are some of the things you've seen in your partner's life as a result of his denial of personal responsibility? Check the applicable consequences and/or add your own.

☐ Loss of intimate fellowship with his wife   ☐ Loss of respect

☐ Loss of deep connection with his children   ☐ Loss of moral compass

☐ Loss of deep connection with Jesus Christ   ☐ Loss of Christian fellowship

☐ Loss of marriage   ☐ Loss of reputation

☐ Loss of relationships with others   ☐ Loss of protection

☐ Loss of financial status   ☐ Loss of hope, joy, and peace

☐ Loss of the blessings of a warm home and family   ☐ _____

☐ Loss of freedom   ☐ _____

Are there ways you may be taking responsibility for your partner's behavior and choices? How?

_____

_____

_____

Are there ways you are protecting your partner from experiencing the natural consequences of his behavior? If so, why do you think you protect him?_____

_____

_____

CAN HE CHANGE?

Lundy Bancroft gives some things to look for in a partner who says they are changing. Don't take their word for it. Ask yourself the following questions (paraphrased from *Why Does He Do That?* By Lundy Bancroft) and circle the answer that best fits.

1. Does he admit fully to what he has done?

Always   Usually   Sometimes   Rarely   Never

2. Has he stopped making excuses and assigning responsibility to you for his behavior?

Always   Usually   Sometimes   Rarely   Never

3. Is he making amends?

Always   Usually   Sometimes   Rarely   Never

4. Is he accepting responsibility and acknowledging that abuse is a choice he is making?

Always   Usually   Sometimes   Rarely   Never

5. Can he identify the specific patterns of controlling behavior he uses?

Always   Usually   Sometimes   Rarely   Never

6. Has he accepted that overcoming his abusiveness will take decades and lots of personal therapy (not couple's counseling)? That he cannot declare himself "cured" in a few months?

Always   Usually   Sometimes   Rarely   Never

7. Is he NOT demanding credit for any improvements he has made? Or is he saying things like, "I haven't done anything in a long time, so it's not a big deal."

Always   Usually   Sometimes   Rarely   Never

8. Is he developing respectful, kind, supportive behaviors that you can FEEL in your relationship?

Always   Usually   Sometimes   Rarely   Never

9. Is he carrying his weight while also sharing power equally with you?

Always   Usually   Sometimes   Rarely   Never

10. Has he changed how he responds to your anger and grievances?

Always   Usually   Sometimes   Rarely   Never

11. Has he changed how he acts in heated conflicts?

Always   Usually   Sometimes   Rarely   Never

12. Is he accepting the consequences of his actions, including not feeling sorry for himself about those consequences and not blaming his partner or children for them.

Always   Usually   Sometimes   Rarely   Never

He is not truly changing unless you can answer *Always* or *Usually* to **every single question**.

Write down what you are thinking and feeling after doing this exercise.

_____

_____

_____

_____

_____

_____

_____

_____

_____

_____

Prayer

Why, O LORD, do you stand far off?—Psalm 10:1a

"God is . . . an ever-present help in trouble" (Ps. 46:1). But He allows trouble to pursue us, as though He were indifferent to its overwhelming pressure, so we may be brought to the end of ourselves. Through the trial, we are led to discover the treasure of darkness and the immeasurable wealth of tribulation.

We may be sure that He who allows the suffering is with us throughout it. It may be that we will only see Him once the ordeal is nearly passed, but we must dare to believe that He never leaves our trial. Our eyes are blinded so we cannot see the One our soul loves. The darkness and our bandages blind us so that we cannot see the form of our High Priest. Yet He is there and is deeply touched.

Let us not rely on our feelings but trust in His unswerving faithfulness. And though we cannot see Him, let us talk to Him. Although His presence is veiled, once we begin to speak to Jesus as if He were literally present, an answering voice comes to show us He is in the shadow, keeping watch over His own.

Your Father is as close to you when you journey through the darkest tunnel as He is when you are under the open heaven!

Cowman, L. B. E., Streams in the Desert (pp. 45-46). Zondervan. Kindle Edition

Lord Jesus,

Be near me right now as I face things that bring such a depth of pain, I can hardly bear up under the weight of it. I'm glad to know that You see me even though I cannot see You. You are familiar with the ache of rejection, slander, and hatred. You know what it is to have your family and closest friends abandon You when You needed them most. You know what it is to have lies circulating about You. Lies You cannot, no matter how hard You would try, make right.

You know what it is to be alone. To work and work with no obvious or immediate gratification. To be betrayed by a close friend. To be called names and treated like an enemy when all You did was spend Your life on behalf of others. Thank You that You walked this road before me, and that all dark paths lead to light and joy and peace one day. Because You conquered sin and death, I have hope. Help me keep my eyes on You.

In Your Name,

Amen

GROUP DISCUSSION QUESTIONS

1. Of the five abusive behaviors covered in chapter four, which two show up the most in your relationship and how?

_____

_____

_____

2. Based solely on your partner's words and behavior, how do you think he views himself? Women? You?

_____

_____

_____

3. What are some of the consequences you see him experiencing as a result of his behaviors? Are there any consequences he is not experiencing because you are protecting him from them? What are those? Why do you think you protect him?

_____

_____

_____

4. Based on the list of things to look for in the "Can He Change?" section of chapter four, is your partner making the necessary belief/behavior changes in order to create a healthier relationship with you? If so, what is he doing?

_____

_____

_____

Week Five

YOUR ROLE

"She knew what bad men looked like. They raped their wives. Or beat them. Or their children. That was how you knew them for what they were. Marco was never that. He never hit her, never forced himself on her, never threatened to shoot her or throw her out an airlock or pour acid in her eyes. He'd pretended kindness so well she would doubt herself, make herself wonder if she was the one being unreasonable, irrational, all the things he implied she was. He never did anything that would have made it easy for her."

JAMES S.A. COREY, NEMESIS GAMES

"You shall be a crown of beauty in the hand of the Lord, and a royal diadem in the hand of your God. You shall no more be termed Forsaken, and your land shall no more be termed Desolate, but you shall be called My Delight Is in Her, and your land Married; for the Lord delights in you, and your land shall be married."

ISAIAH 62:3-4 (ESV)

"You are altogether beautiful, my darling; there is no flaw in you."

SOLOMON 4:7

READING ASSIGNMENT

Chapter Five: Your Role

SUMMARY POINTS:

1. Most victims are targeted for their strengths.

2. Victims lose themselves when they begin to get their identity from their abuser.

3. There are a variety of tools a victim uses to cope with the abuse.

4. One of the most common results of long term emotional abuse is complex post-traumatic stress disorder.

WHEN YOU ARE FINISHED WITH WORKBOOK CHAPTER FIVE YOU WILL:

- Be able to identify your own strengths and see how they have been used against you.

- Recognize which coping strategies have kept you stuck.

- Identify possible symptoms of C-PTSD.

MINING FOR GOLD

1. What was the golden nugget you found in chapter five? Write down a favorite quote or new idea.

_____

_____

_____

_____

2. What did you believe before you read this chapter?

_____

_____

_____

_____

3. How were your prior beliefs challenged in this chapter?

_____

_____

_____

_____

4. How will the golden nugget you discovered help your life look different ten years from now?

_____

_____

_____

_____

SELF-ASSESSMENT EXERCISE

Emotional and spiritual abuse survivors often take their identity from their abusive partner or family of origin, and it isn't pretty. But the fact is, survivors are often emotionally intelligent, sensitive, strong, discerning people. They are targeted for their strengths. Let's look at some of the strengths listed in chapter five and see how you use those strengths in your life and in your survival process.

After each strength, write down an example or two of how you demonstrate that strength in your relationships. (You can read the more detailed descriptions in chapter five.)

1. She is considerate of others and puts the needs of others before her own. _____
_____
_____
_____

2. She is persevering and faithful to her commitments. _____
_____
_____
_____

3. She is trustworthy, open, honest, and forthright. _____
_____
_____
_____

4. She takes responsibility for herself and those around her. _____
_____
_____
_____

5. She is generous with her love, her time, her energy, and her resources. _____
_____
_____
_____

6. She is kind and empathic, deeply caring about how others feel and her own effect on their feelings.

_____

_____

_____

7. She is intuitive—sensitive to the emotional environment around her. _____

_____

_____

_____

8. She is forgiving—even when others aren't sorry and don't ask. _____

_____

_____

_____

9. She is patient and long-suffering—always hoping others can grow and change. _____

_____

_____

_____

10. She is courageous. She keeps getting up every morning with new hope and resolve to do her best.

_____

_____

_____

11. She is loyal and doesn't want to betray her abuser. _____

_____

_____

_____

COPING SKILLS

In this exercise we will look at ten coping skills survivors use to help them get through life with an abuser. As you heal, you will rely less and less on these coping skills. I'd like you to rate how much you think you use each coping skill. A one means you don't use that coping skill at all and a ten means you use it all the time. Then I'd like you to come back in one year and rate yourself again to see how much you've grown!

Today's Date: _____

1. I blame myself when things go wrong in my relationship.

    1   2   3   4   5   6   7   8   9   10

    One year later _____

    1   2   3   4   5   6   7   8   9   10

2. I deny things are really as bad as they probably are. "He's not that bad, and sometimes he's pretty nice."

    1   2   3   4   5   6   7   8   9   10

    One year later _____

    1   2   3   4   5   6   7   8   9   10

3. I normalize my partner's bad behavior. "All guys do what he does."

    1   2   3   4   5   6   7   8   9   10

    One year later _____

    1   2   3   4   5   6   7   8   9   10

4. I rationalize his bad behavior. "He had a bad day."

    1   2   3   4   5   6   7   8   9   10

    One year later _____

    1   2   3   4   5   6   7   8   9   10

5. I spiritualize my pain. "I'm trusting God to change him."

    1   2   3   4   5   6   7   8   9   10

    One year later _____

    1   2   3   4   5   6   7   8   9   10

6. I forget what he does or says and just want to move on.

                                1 2 3 4 5 6 7 8 9 10

One year later _____

                                1 2 3 4 5 6 7 8 9 10

7. I minimize the impact of his behavior on my life. "At least he plays with the kids."

                                1 2 3 4 5 6 7 8 9 10

One year later _____

                                1 2 3 4 5 6 7 8 9 10

8. I distract myself with ministry, homemaking, work, or other activities.

                                1 2 3 4 5 6 7 8 9 10

One year later _____

                                1 2 3 4 5 6 7 8 9 10

9. I lower my expectations thinking that if I expect very little, I won't be disappointed.

                                1 2 3 4 5 6 7 8 9 10

One year later _____

                                1 2 3 4 5 6 7 8 9 10

10. I hold on to hope that one day he will change.

                                1 2 3 4 5 6 7 8 9 10

One year later _____

                                1 2 3 4 5 6 7 8 9 10

Pick the one or two coping skills you use most often and brainstorm some practical ways you can work on bringing that number down over the next year.

_____

_____

_____

_____

_____

_____

_____

_____

_____

_____

_____

_____

_____

_____

_____

_____

_____

_____

_____

YOUR IDENTITY

1. Describe how you were treated as a child. Were you usually valued and treated affectionately, or were you more generally treated as annoying or naughty or only good when you were meeting the needs of other people in your life?_____

    _____

    _____

2. How did the way you were treated affect the way you viewed yourself back then? _____

    _____

    _____

3. How do you think your childhood may have caused you to be vulnerable to being attracted to an emotionally abusive man? _____

    _____

    _____

4. Thinking about your life today, as an adult, how has your marriage relationship mirrored the way you were raised? _____

    _____

    _____

5. If important people in your life have communicated that you can never be good enough, do you believe them? Why or why not?_____

    _____

    _____

6. Was it hard to read that, in his mind, you have to fail in order for him to succeed? How does it feel to recognize that his goal is to get you to experience shame and self-loathing so he can feel okay about himself?

    _____

    _____

ASSESSING YOUR RISK OF HAVING C-PTSD

Let's review the three ingredients that cause C-PTSD.

1. Repeated trauma over a long period of time.

   How long have you been married?_____

2. The belief that there is no way of escape.

   Have you been taught that God hates divorce?   Yes   No

   Have you held this belief?   Yes   No

3. The lack of outside support, validation, and help.

   Who knows you are suffering?_____

   Do you have confidants who believe and support you? If so, write their names here:

   _____

   _____

   _____

   Are there people you've told who have not believed or supported you? Write their names here:

   _____

   _____

   _____

EMOTIONAL PROBLEMS

Put a check mark by the symptoms you struggle with.

☐ I have difficulty regulating my emotions.

☐ I get triggered easily.

☐ I experience persistent anxiety.

☐ I have difficulty remembering events surrounding an abusive incident.

☐ I relive experiences over and over in an effort to solve the problem.

☐ I often experience feelings of helplessness and hopelessness.

☐ It's hard for me to take initiative.

☐ I feel shame.

☐ I feel guilt.

☐ I feel self-blame.

☐ I have a sense of being different from everyone else.

☐ I believe my abuser is more powerful than I am.

☐ I am preoccupied with my relationship to my abuser.

☐ I alternate between feeling of revenge and anger toward my abuser and feelings of relief and gratefulness to him.

☐ I feel allied with my abuser and experience a sense of relief when I just give in and accept his version of reality.

☐ I often rationalize the abuse.

☐ I am constantly hoping and searching for someone to rescue me. Someone who will listen and validate my experience. I have the feeling that unless someone else believes me, maybe what I'm going through isn't really happening.

☐ I am not able to protect myself.

☐ Sometimes I feel despairing of the future.

☐ Sometimes I feel numb and void of emotion while at other times I feel terrified and confused.

Physical Health Problems

Put a check mark by the symptoms you struggle with.

☐ I have been diagnosed with depression and/or anxiety.

☐ I have digestive issues.

☐ I have chronic fatigue syndrome or fibromyalgia.

☐ I have chronic headaches.

☐ I have back and neck problems.

☐ I have vision problems.

☐ I have heart palpitations.

☐ I have panic attacks.

☐ I have asthma.

☐ I have high stress.

☐ My immune system doesn't work very well.

☐ I have endocrine issues.

☐ My hormones are not balanced.

☐ I have brain fog.

If you think you may have C-PTSD, I recommend that you consider finding a therapist who is skilled in helping people heal. The good news is that C-PTSD is something that can be overcome.

Recommended Resources

Complex PTSD: From Surviving to Thriving by Pete Walker

The PTSD Workbook by Mary Beth Williams

PRAYER

(Say this out loud.)

Dear Heavenly Father,

Are not two sparrows sold for a copper coin? And not one of them falls to the ground apart from your will. But the very hairs of my head are all numbered. Therefore I will not be afraid; because I am of more value than many sparrows to You. —Matthew 10:29-31

My Dear Daughter,

For I know the thoughts I think toward you, thoughts of peace and not of evil, to give you a future and a hope. — Jeremiah 29:11

Dear Heavenly Father,

For I am persuaded that neither death nor life, nor angels nor principalities nor powers, nor things present nor things to come, nor height nor depth, nor any other created thing, shall be able to separate me from Your love which is in Christ Jesus my Lord. —Romans 8:38-39

My Dear Daughter,

Be strong and of good courage; do not be afraid, nor be dismayed, for I am with you wherever you go. —Joshua 1:9

Dear Heavenly Father,

Your eyes saw my substance, being yet unformed. And in Your book they all were written, the days fashioned for me, when as yet there were none of them. How precious also are Your thoughts to me, O God! How great is the sum of them! —Psalm 139:16-17

My Dear Daughter,

I chose you before the foundation of the world, that you should be holy and without blame before Me in love, having predestined you to adoption like a first born son, according to the good pleasure of My will... —Ephesians 1:4-5

Dear Heavenly Father,

Thank you that I am my beloved's and my beloved is mine. —Song of Solomon 2:16

I will put my hope in You, Amen.

GROUP DISCUSSION QUESTIONS

1. Was it surprising to learn that you may be an emotional abuse victim because of your strengths? Why or why not?

_____

_____

_____

_____

2. Share two of your strengths and how they were used against you in your relationship in order to control and hurt you.

_____

_____

_____

3. What are some of the coping skills you have used the most in your relationship and why?

_____

_____

_____

4. Are you experiencing any symptoms of C-PTSD? Have you done anything to get help for that (i.e. therapy, exercises, small group therapy, books, etc..)? If so, how have the things you've done to heal been helpful or unhelpful?

_____

_____

_____

_____

Week Six

THE ROLES OF OTHERS

"There are going to be truckloads of people who will see the light in you before you see it. They are going to see the tree inside of your seed before you even realize that it's going to be a tree one day. But they're not going to bend over and reach down towards the flame to say 'I see you, keep glowing.' They're not going to kneel down and tap the ground and say to the seed 'I see you, keep reaching.' Instead, they're going to try and snuff out the flame; they're going to try and drown the seed. Lest you see your brightness; lest you realize you will one day bear fruit! It's tragic, because, how do you protect what you can't even see? Put your hand to your chest and feel the warmth of your light; press your palm to the Earth and feel the throbbing of the seed that is you; close your eyes, child, and never leave you!"

C. JoyBell C.

"But understand this, that in the last days there will come times of difficulty. For people will be lovers of self, lovers of money, proud, arrogant, abusive, disobedient to their parents, ungrateful, unholy, heartless, unappeasable, slanderous, without self-control, brutal, not loving good, treacherous, reckless, swollen with conceit, lovers of pleasure rather than lovers of God, having the appearance of godliness, but denying its power. Avoid such people."

II Timothy 3:1-5 (ESV)

"A new commandment I give to you, that you love one another: just as I have loved you, you also are to love one another. By this all people will know that you are my disciples, if you have love for one another."

John 13:34-35 (ESV)

READING ASSIGNMENT

Chapter Six: The Roles of Others

SUMMARY POINTS:

1. God created all humans—regardless of gender, race, or socioeconomic status—equal, not just equally valuable.

2. The collective, quiet agreement of the masses who refuse to stand against abuse contribute the MOST to perpetuating abuse in our culture.

3. Many churches are more invested in protecting and supporting a marriage than they are in protecting and supporting a human life.

4. Bible counseling often contributes to the re-abuse of women and children in the church and home.

5. Friends and family will support us as long as we help maintain the status quo. Opening up about abuse often invites criticism and loss of relationship with those who are uncomfortable with the truth.

WHEN YOU ARE FINISHED WITH WORKBOOK CHAPTER SIX YOU WILL:

*   Be able to assess your own risk of being re-abused.

*   Identify the underlying reasons your church may support your partner in his abuse of you.

*   Be able to decide if your therapist is a good fit for you or not.

*   Have a deeper understanding of why some people respond the way they do when you disclose abuse.

MINING FOR GOLD

1. What was the golden nugget you found in chapter six? Write down a favorite quote or new idea.

_____

_____

_____

_____

2. What did you believe before you read this chapter?

_____

_____

_____

_____

3. How were your prior beliefs challenged in this chapter?

_____

_____

_____

_____

4. How will the golden nugget you discovered help your life look different ten years from now?

_____

_____

_____

_____

RE-ABUSE RISK ASSESSMENT

1. My family of origin is emotionally healthy, and they see what is happening and will support me if I take steps to protect myself, including the steps of separation and divorce.

    Yes   Maybe   No

2. I attend a church that believes in the equality and worth of women.

    Yes   Maybe   No

3. The leaders in my church lovingly support people through separation and divorce.

    Yes   Maybe   No

4. There is a "no tolerance" policy at my church when it comes to every kind of abuse.

    Yes   Maybe   No

5. I am seeing (or will see) an educated, trained, experienced, and licensed counselor who understands abuse and C-PTSD.

    Yes   Maybe   No

6. Most of my friends have healthy boundaries and are not controlling or manipulative or critical of others.

    Yes   Maybe   No

Did you answer YES to all six? If so, your risk of being re-abused is very low. You've got a healthy team of people to support you no matter what you decide to do.

Did you answer MAYBE or NO to four or more of the above questions? If so, your risk of being re-abused is high by at least 1-2 groups of people. You will want to be prepared for this by understanding why re-abuse occurs and how to respond to it.

EVALUATE YOUR CHURCH

1. What does your church believe about the roles of men and women within marriage? _____

   _____

   _____

   _____

   _____

2. What does your church believe about divorce and remarriage? _____

   _____

   _____

   _____

   _____

3. What do you think your church believes about the reality and serious destructiveness of emotional abuse?

   _____

   _____

   _____

   _____

4. Do you feel like your church views the institution of marriage itself as more important than the people in the marriage? _____

   _____

   _____

   _____

   _____

5. Does your church focus on changing the abuser to save the marriage, or on rescuing the victim from being further harmed by the abuser? _____

_____

_____

_____

_____

6. How likely do you think those beliefs will serve (or already have served) as a motivation for them to support you when you report emotional or spiritual abuse by your partner?_____

_____

_____

_____

_____

7. If your church does not support you, how do you think you'll respond and why? (Or how DID you respond if this has already happened in the past and why did you respond that way?) _____

_____

_____

_____

_____

WHAT TO EXPECT WHEN YOU DISCLOSE ABUSE AND TRY TO GET HELP

Fill in the blanks with answers found in chapter six.

1. When a victim comes forward for help, she needs to be _____ and _____ and _____ SAFE.

2. But the number ONE priority of the church is often to _____ the _____.

3. The church's number TWO priority is to _____ the _____ in order to achieve the number one priority.

4. The _____ is almost always the one who wants to save the marriage.

5. The victim's goal is to stop _____, stop _____, walk in _____, set healthy _____, get away from _____, and pursue _____.

6. In order to justify their _____ of the victim, a church does exactly what the victim's _____ has done for decades—_____ and _____ her.

7. When a church's agenda for this process of helping a victim has to end with an _____ _____ and a happily-ever-after _____, the process is doomed from the beginning.

8. The _____ holds out a different option.

9. When a woman comes forward needing help in a healthy, Christ-centered church, she will be _____ and _____ right where she is. She will be _____ as a precious human being with rights to her own _____ and her own _____. Her _____ will be respected.

"Your love for one another will prove to the world that you are my disciples." John 13:35 (NLT)

Based on what you know of Jesus in Scripture, describe the response He would have to your daughter or other loved one seeking help from an abusive partner. _____

_____

_____

DO YOU HAVE A GOOD COUNSELOR?

If you don't have a counselor, you can skip this section and come back to it another time when you are looking for a counselor or assessing a new one.

1. My counselor is licensed in my state to do therapy.

Yes   No

2. My counselor is experienced in helping people with trauma recovery.

Yes   No

3. My counselor is licensed to give clinical level tests to diagnose things like PTSD.

Yes   No

4. My counselor is trained in a wide variety of therapy modalities and is continuing his/her education by keeping up with new evidence-based treatments.

Yes   No

5. My counselor is familiar with narcissistic abuse, emotional abuse, and spiritual abuse and has successfully treated victims of these types of abuse.

Yes   No

6. My counselor would not recommend couple's counseling for marriages that present with abuse issues.

Yes (true)   No (false)

7. I feel very comfortable and safe with my counselor.

Yes   No

8. There is a good balance of empathy, understanding, and insight along with practical tools to help me in between sessions.

Yes   No

9. My counselor is effective at giving me hope for my healing and for my future.

Yes   No

10. My counselor takes good notes and keeps me moving forward.

Yes   No

11. My counselor is not focused on saving my marriage but on saving (helping) me.

Yes   No

If you could answer YES to 10-11 of these,
then you probably have a therapist that is a good fit for you.

If you could answer YES to 8-9 of these, then you may have a good therapist,
but she may not be a good fit for you personally.

If you can answer YES to seven or less of these,
you may need to find a new therapist.

DEALING WITH FRIENDS AND FAMILY

Always remember that how people respond to us tells us about who they are. Their responses do not tell us anything about who we are. With that in mind, let's explore how people have responded to what you're going through (or have gone through).

1. What have you specifically shared about your marriage issues with some of the most important people in your life? _____

_____

_____

_____

_____

_____

2. What kind of responses were you hoping to get? _____

_____

_____

_____

_____

_____

3. What are some of the positive responses you've received, and why do you think those particular people responded in a way that was supportive of your life and boundaries? _____

_____

_____

_____

_____

_____

4. What are some of the negative responses you've received, and why do you think those particular people responded in a way that was unsupportive and disrespectful of your boundaries? _____

_____

_____

_____

_____

_____

_____

5. What have you learned about the different people closest to you? _____

_____

_____

_____

_____

_____

_____

_____

6. How will that knowledge affect your life moving forward? _____

_____

_____

_____

_____

_____

_____

LOOKING THROUGH THE LENS OF JESUS

1. Read these verses out loud.

   "When he saw the crowds, he had compassion for them, because they were harassed and helpless, like sheep without a shepherd." Matthew 9:36

   "Be merciful, just as your Father is merciful." Luke 6:36

2. Think of the last situation where someone close to you responded negatively and hurtfully to the things you shared about your situation. Close your eyes and try to put yourself back in that experience. Picture where you were and where the other person was. Perhaps it was an e-mail. Imagine that you are on your phone reading that e-mail. Remember what you were feeling and thinking.

3. Open your eyes and read the two verses above again. Out loud.

4. Close your eyes again and insert the Person of Jesus in your experience. Where is He? What is He doing? What is He saying to you? Take some time to fully re-imagine this experience with Jesus as part of it.

5. Describe what you just experienced: _____

_____

_____

_____

_____

_____

_____

_____

_____

_____

PRAYER

Write your own prayer below. Some ideas to process with Jesus may include:

- how you are feeling at this point in your journey.
- questions you have for Him.
- lament for the sorrow and grief you are experiencing.
- thanksgiving for the insights He is giving you so you can move forward.
- your longings and wishes for a different future of freedom and joy.
- your fears about what is happening now and what may happen in the future.

Dear Jesus,

_____

_____

_____

_____

_____

_____

_____

_____

_____

_____

_____

_____

_____

_____

_____

GROUP DISCUSSION QUESTIONS

1. Describe your own experience with your church. Have you told anyone there yet? Have you tried to get help? If so, how did that go?

_____

_____

_____

_____

2. If you've had experiences with counselors of any type, positive or negative, share those experiences with the group.

_____

_____

_____

_____

3. How have your family and/or friends supported or not supported you on your journey?

_____

_____

_____

_____

Week Seven

GOD'S ROLE

"We need to remember that God delivers His people not just from their own sin but also from injustices. When God speaks to Moses out of the burning bush, He says 'I am the God of your fathers, I have observed the misery of my people, I have heard their cry on account of their oppressors. I know their sufferings, and I have come down to deliver them.' God introduces Himself to His people as their deliverer and protector. God asks His people repeatedly in Scripture to work for justice and righteousness. This is who we, as worshippers of God, are told to be, people who do justice. God calls us to confront oppression but also to provide protection and care for the vulnerable. We see Jesus doing these things. He identifies with the powerless, takes up their cause, and stands against those who do harm to the vulnerable. This is who we are to be, deliverers and protectors."

BECOMING A CHURCH THAT CARES WELL FOR THE ABUSED
DARBY STRICKLAND

"You cover the Lord's altar with tears, with weeping and groaning because he no longer regards the offering or accepts it with favor from your hand. But you say, 'Why does he not?' Because the Lord was witness between you and the wife of your youth, to whom you have been faithless, though she is your companion and your wife by covenant."

MALACHI 2:13-14 (ESV)

"O Lord, you hear the desire of the afflicted; you will strengthen their heart; you will incline your ear to do justice to the fatherless and the oppressed, so that man who is of the earth may strike terror no more."

PSALM 10:17-18 (ESV)

Reading Assignment

Chapter Seven: God's Role

Summary Points:

1. God created women to be "Ezer Kenegdo." Warriors corresponding to men. Not "helpers suitable" for them, as some gender-biased translations say.

2. The vast majority of Bible references to our life as believers do not distinguish between male and female, and the ones that do are often translated through modern 21st century perspectives rather than through the lens of the historical time period in which they were written when Christianity was in its infant stages.

3. Abusive patriarchal theology teaches the same two lies Satan told in the garden. 1. God isn't good. 2. You have no value. God is good to men but not women. Women have value only insomuch as they prove their value through good works toward men.

4. God is nothing like your abusers and their allies. He does not condone abuse. He warns against wolves in sheep's clothing and calls abusers frauds.

5. Jesus was abused and knows exactly what you are going through.

6. Marriage is not a protected space for evil.

7. God set up divorce as a merciful way out for victims of abuse.

When you are finished with Workbook Chapter Seven you will:

- Be able to articulate God's view of women.

- Understand how God views you, personally.

- Know seven ways God hates abuse and why.

- Be able to summarize your life from a bird's eye view.

- See how divorce fits into God's compassionate plan for victims of abuse.

MINING FOR GOLD

1. What was the golden nugget you found in chapter seven? Write down a favorite quote or new idea.

_____

_____

_____

_____

2. What did you believe before you read this chapter?

_____

_____

_____

_____

3. How were your prior beliefs challenged in this chapter?

_____

_____

_____

_____

4. How will the golden nugget you discovered help your life look different ten years from now?

_____

_____

_____

_____

God's View of Women

1. You may have learned that a woman is a man's "help meet" (Genesis 2:18). Someone who will help him do all the things God has called him to do. Is this something you've believed or currently believe? If so, how has this belief had an effect on your marriage and your life?

2. In Hebrew, "Ezer Kenegdo" (Genesis 2:18) actually means "warrior corresponding to him." In your mind, how does that paint a different picture of your place in this world? Describe what a woman who is a true "Ezer Kenegdo" would be like. Can you think of any examples in the Bible?

3. "For you are all sons of God through faith in Christ Jesus… there is neither male nor female; for you are all one in Christ Jesus." (Galatians 3:26, 28; NASB)

What is God telling His people in these verses? What is He saying to His daughters? _____

_____

_____

_____

God's View of You

1. Close your eyes and imagine yourself by a quiet stream of water. You can hear the wind softly rustling the leaves, the water gurgling, birds calling to each other, the chirps of frogs, and the hum of insects. You see Jesus standing by the stream, and He looks up at you. Describe what you think He is seeing. How do you think you look to Him? What might He be thinking? What are you thinking? What is He feeling? What are you feeling? Do you trust Him? Are you angry? Do you question His power? His love? His ability to help? Be brutally honest about what is going on in this scene.

_____

_____

_____

_____

_____

2. Remember the story in our book about how Jesus responded to His mother, Mary, when she went around Him in order to force a miracle and make more wine for the wedding? What is your first reaction to that story now that it has been presented in a new light? _____

_____

_____

_____

_____

How do you feel about what Mary did? _____

_____

_____

_____

How do you feel about how Jesus responded? _____

_____

_____

_____

What did this story teach you about Jesus? _____

_____

_____

_____

What did this story teach you about yourself? _____

_____

_____

_____

GOD'S VIEW OF ABUSE

Let's go over what the Bible says about how God feels when He sees the abuse of human lives. And let's bring it home to what He feels when he sees the abuse you have endured.

1. God hates abuse (Proverbs 6:16-19).

    Think of the last time you experienced an abusive incident where you were looked down on (haughty eyes), lied to (lying tongue), hated (shed innocent blood – hate is the same as murder), gaslit (heart that devises wicked plans), raged at (feet that make haste to evil), gossiped and lied about (false witness who breathes out lies), or baited (one who sows discord among brothers). Describe how God felt when He saw another person do that to you.

    _____

    _____

    _____

2. God says an abuser is a fraud and his religion is worthless (James 1:26).

    Think of the times when Bible verses were used to shame and control you. Does your abuser have credibility in God's eyes? Why or why not? And what does God think about your abuser's devotion to Him?

    _____

    _____

    _____

3. God says abusers and those who justify them are an abomination (Proverbs 17:15).

    How does God feel about the religious people in your life who have chosen to believe your abuser while alienating you from love and support?

    _____

    _____

    _____

4. God says verbal abuse harms people and carries the power of death (Proverbs 13:20; 18:21).

    Does God take the verbal and emotional abuse you have gone through seriously? Why?

    _____

    _____

    _____

5. God says emotional abuse is a heavy burden to bear up under (Proverbs 27:3; 18:14).

    What does God think about the burdens you've been carrying on your back for so many years?

    _____

    _____

    _____

6. God says there will be a high price to pay for people who damage their children through abuse (Matthew 18:6).

    What does God think about the kinds of abuse that turn children away from Him when they grow up?

    _____

    _____

    _____

7. God says emotional abuse is just like being gutted with a knife (Proverbs 12:18).

    What does this tell you about the effects of emotional abuse and what God thinks about that kind of abuse and the damage it does?

    _____

    _____

    _____

Read this paragraph from the book:

"As victims of abuse, it's easy to become entangled in a hopeless quest of trying to fix an abuser, help him, and cure him—but we could as easily raise the dead! There is only one Savior. We cannot save ourselves by our own good works, and we do not have the power to save anyone else, especially our abusers. We must submit to God who is Almighty—who is more than able both to protect us from evil and to do whatever He pleases with evildoers. We must come to Him as our good Father who always has another chapter for our stories and who gives us the courage and strength to close and bar the door against evil."

Think of your life as a story book with chapters. If your story had ten chapters, one chapter for each decade, and you were guaranteed to live for 100 years, what would those chapters be called? Try to write the titles of chapters you haven't lived yet as well!

Chapter One: _____

Chapter Two: _____

Chapter Three: _____

Chapter Four: _____

Chapter Five: _____

Chapter Six: _____

Chapter Seven: _____

Chapter Eight: _____

Chapter Nine: _____

Chapter Ten: _____

GOD'S VIEW OF MARRIAGE

There were seven lies about marriage presented in chapter seven. They are as follows:

1. The ultimate goal for a woman is an intimate relationship with a man in marriage.
2. Marriage is forever.
3. A married woman belongs to her husband.
4. A married woman is ruled by her husband.
5. A married woman's responsibility is to make her husband happy.
6. A woman can change her husband.
7. All marriages are good and should be saved at all costs for the glory of God.

Pick three of the lies you have believed and write about why you believed those lies as well as how those lies have had an effect on your life.

Lie Number One: _____

Lie Number Two: _____

Lie Number Three: _____

GOD AND DIVORCE

Fill in the blanks from this section in chapter seven:

1. Biblically, there are _____ types of covenants: _____ and _____.

2. In _____ covenants, one person bears all the _____ for keeping all the terms of the covenant. Since God keeps His _____ covenants perfectly, they cannot be _____.

3. But the _____ covenant is a _____ covenant. In the _____ Covenant, _____ partners take vows to _____, _____, _____, forsake all others, and remain _____ until death.

4. If the _____ covenant has been violated according to Biblical guidelines (adultery, _____, or _____), then you, the one who has been _____ against, can rightfully declare the covenant to be _____ and _____. This declaration is called _____.

5. Divorce is not the _____ of the marriage. Divorce is the _____ that the marriage has already been _____.

6. According to Jeremiah 3:8, when Israel broke their end of a two-way covenant with God, God _____ His people.

7. I Corinthians 7:13-16 indicates that _____ is covenant-breaking grounds for _____.

8. The creation of _____ that are too harsh to live in is a _____ type of _____ or desertion.

9. The Bible _____ says "God hates divorce." Translated correctly, it states that God hates _____ away. (This was the egregious practice in the Old Testament whereby men could simply leave their wife and take a new one. The law required him to give her a "certificate of divorce" so she was free to remarry and be provided for. "Putting away" was this practice of abandoning a woman while also withholding that certificate of divorce. Much the same way that modern abusers emotionally abandon their wives but refuse to divorce them so they are free to remarry and be loved and provided for.)

10. An _____ marriage does _____ represent Christ and the church.

Prayer

Dear Heavenly Father,

Thank You for Your loving provision for those who are hurting, dehumanized, abandoned, treated disrespectfully, mocked, looked down on, shamed, taken advantage of, lied to, stolen from, cheated on, and hated.

You not only see me and others like me, but You love us with an unshakeable, unstoppable love. Nothing can separate me from Your love. You created me and then bought me with the blood of Your Son, Jesus Christ, and I belong to YOU alone. I do not belong to my spouse, my church, or anyone or anything on this earth. I am Yours.

In You I have freedom to take responsibility for my life and take care of my mind, my spirit, and my body. You want me to do this. You've given this responsibility to me, alone—and to no-one else. Help me to love what You love. To cherish what You cherish. I have not always done that. I've hated myself. I've been angry at myself. I've felt sad and sorry for myself, but I haven't always taken the steps I needed to protect myself. Instead, I have listened to the voices of men and women. Their opinions have meant so much to me, and Your opinion has meant little by comparison.

To know that You want to see me safe and free, fulfilling all the purpose for which You created me, leaves me feeling hopeful. But it also leaves me fearful. I'm afraid of how to get there. I'm afraid of what I may have to do. What kinds of choices I may need to make. I'm afraid of change. I'm afraid of more rejection. I'm afraid of loss. I'm afraid I'm not strong enough.

I am not enough. It's the same lie I've always believed. The lie that I'm not worth it. That I'm a bad person. That I'll never measure up. I try and try, but I can't do it. And now I feel the same when I think about the future. What if…what if I fail myself? What if I fail You?

*"Yet I am always with you; you hold me by my right hand. You guide me with your counsel, and afterward you will take me into glory. Whom have I in heaven but you? And earth has nothing I desire besides you. **My flesh and my heart may fail, but God is the strength of my heart and my portion forever.** Those who are far from you will perish; you destroy all who are unfaithful to you. But as for me, it is good to be near God. I have made the Sovereign Lord my refuge; I will tell of all your deeds."* Psalm 73: 23-28

Thank You that even when I fail, You never fail. Your mercies are brand new every morning. Your faithfulness is great toward me. You do not see me as a failure, but as your precious, good-enough daughter whom You delight in.

Amen

GROUP DISCUSSION QUESTIONS

1. What was one of the most surprising messages from this chapter to you? Are there any in particular you'd want to make sure your daughter or another young woman you care about knows and understands?

   _____

   _____

   _____

   _____

2. How has God shown up in the midst of your pain over the years?

   _____

   _____

   _____

   _____

3. Describe your current relationship with God. How did your relationship with Him get to this point? Where do you see it going in the future?

   _____

   _____

   _____

   _____

4. Share one new thing you learned from this chapter that is changing the way you think of God and His view of you and your marriage.

   _____

   _____

   _____

Week Eight

CHANGING YOUR ROLE

"We change our behavior when the pain of staying the same becomes greater than the pain of changing. Consequences give us the pain that motivates us to change."

DR. HENRY CLOUD & DR. JOHN TOWNSEND

"See, I am doing a new thing! Now it springs up; do you not perceive it? I am making a way in the wilderness and streams in the wasteland."

ISAIAH 43:19

"Praise the LORD, my soul; all my inmost being, praise his holy name.

Praise the LORD, my soul, and forget not all his benefits—

who forgives all your sins and heals all your diseases,

who redeems your life from the pit and crowns you with love and compassion,

who satisfies your desires with good things so that your youth is renewed like the eagle's."

PSALM 103:1-5

Reading Assignment

Chapter Eight: Changing Your Role

Summary Points:

1. Instead of spinning your wheels trying to get another person to change, what if you put all that same effort into changing your role?

2. Boundaries are the key to an emotionally healthy and satisfying life. God doesn't expect you to take care of your husband's "home and yard." He expects you to wisely steward your own.

3. The idea of church authority is cultural, not biblical. Men and women who follow Jesus Christ have one authority. Jesus Christ.

4. The first step in creating change in our lives is to acknowledge that we do have choices, we do make choices, and they are our own choices.

5. You don't need the agreement, approval, or permission of anyone else to steward your life before God.

6. It's okay to be human and make mistakes. That's how we learn.

7. When you come to a fork in the road, it's not always the path to heaven or the path to hell.

8. You cannot know the future; therefore, you cannot make decisions based on predictions of that unknown future.

9. It is not a mark of spiritual maturity to suffer needlessly.

10. You don't need to be rescued. You need to be empowered to be the adult woman you are.

When you are finished with Workbook Chapter Eight you will:

*   See the ways you spend your time and energy on others vs. yourself.

*   Understand how to take responsibility for what is yours and let go of responsibility for what isn't.

*   Discover the ways you are and aren't living authentically.

*   Gain insights into your thought processes regarding authority and decision making.

MINING FOR GOLD

1. What was the golden nugget you found in chapter eight? Write down a favorite quote or new idea.

_____

_____

_____

_____

2. What did you believe before you read this chapter?

_____

_____

_____

_____

3. How were your prior beliefs challenged in this chapter?

_____

_____

_____

_____

4. How will the golden nugget you discovered help your life look different ten years from now?

_____

_____

_____

_____

A New Focus

In one column make a list of the things you have done to support, serve, help, and change your partner so he can be the best version of himself. In the second column make a list of all the things you have done to support, serve, help, and change yourself so you can be the best version of yourself.

My Partner	Myself
Example: I listen to his perspective and consider it.	*I respect my perspective as well.*
Example: I encourage him to get individual therapy.	*I also get my own therapy.*

1. Is there anything you notice about the difference in time, energy, and resources that you invest in your partner versus in yourself? _____

_____

_____

_____

_____

_____

2. Do you think it is possible to change another person? If so, how? If not, why not? _____

_____

_____

_____

_____

_____

3. Moving forward, would you want those two columns to change in any way? If so, how? _____

_____

_____

_____

_____

_____

BOUNDARIES

Circle the things you are responsible for in your life. Put a box around the things your husband is responsible for in his life. (Or you can use different colored highlighters!)

Your beliefs	Your schedule	His paycheck	His haircut
The way you dress	How you drive a car	How he talks to the waitress	How he handles conflict
His schedule	His beliefs	Your happiness	What you watch on TV
The food you eat	What he wears	How he talks to you	How he spends his free time
Your paycheck	Your haircut	Your relationships	Who you go out with
His volunteer work at church	The food he eats	Your health	Where he goes after work
His feelings about his job	His happiness	How he drives a car	His relationships
His health	Your feelings about your job	What you make for the church potluck	

Add some more of your own.

What are YOU responsible for in your life? _____

_____

_____

What is HE responsible for in his life? _____

_____

_____

What insights did you get doing this exercise, and how will that change the way you view your life moving forward? _____

_____

_____

AUTHORITY

1. Prior to reading chapter eight, what have you historically believed about the role of authority in your own life? _____

   _____

   _____

   _____

2. List some people who had authority over you and describe how they used their authority to help or harm you. _____

   _____

   _____

   _____

3. According to chapter eight, what is the role of someone who has been placed in an authority position (teacher, pastor, police officer, parent, etc.)? _____

   _____

   _____

   _____

4. What do the following verses teach us about authority from God's perspective?

   "And Jesus came and said to them, 'All authority in heaven and on earth has been given to me." Matthew 28:18 (ESV)

   "But Peter and the apostles answered, 'We must obey God rather than men.'" Acts 5:29 (ESV)

   _____

   _____

   _____

   _____

YOUR RESPONSIBILITY TO CHOOSE

1. Do you share power in your marriage relationship? If so, how? If not, why not?_____

    _____

    _____

2. If you began to make your own choices for your life, what would you risk losing? Are you willing to risk losing those things? _____

    _____

    _____

3. Sometimes we have choices, but they are all hard, and they all have serious consequences. In those situations we have to decide what is best for us (and our children) at that time. We may make a different choice later on when things change. It's okay to assess your situation and make different choices depending on different circumstances or the timing of things. Is there a choice like this that you are facing in your own life right now? Describe that choice and what hangs in the balance.

    _____

    _____

    _____

    _____

    _____

    _____

    _____

    _____

    _____

    _____

Fill in the blanks and then write your thoughts about each statement. (You could write "Because…" and create a truth statement for yourself.)

1. You don't need the _____, approval, or _____ of other human beings to steward your life before God.

_____

_____

_____

2. It's okay to be _____ and make _____.

_____

_____

_____

3. When you come to a _____ in the road, it's not always the path to _____ or the path to _____.

_____

_____

_____

4. You cannot know the _____; therefore, you cannot make _____ based on _____ of that unknown future.

_____

_____

_____

AIMING FOR AUTHENTICITY

Put a check-mark by the statements that are mostly true or completely true of you. This is not to show you where you are failing, but rather to show you where you are healthy and where you need some tender-loving care. Your job moving forward will be to nurture your spirit back to health in these areas.

☐ I don't put people on pedestals. Everyone has problems and fails in different ways.

☐ I honor God before men.

☐ I will disobey the letter of the law if obedience means I must harm another human being.

☐ I'm okay with not being perfect.

☐ I don't expect others to be perfect.

☐ I am not afraid to make decisions.

☐ I speak out against injustice even though I get ridiculed or shamed.

☐ I don't feel ashamed of who I am.

☐ I don't chase after love and acceptance at the expense of my well-being.

☐ I don't try to attract the spiritual or popular crowd.

☐ I love and appreciate myself.

☐ If I don't please people, that's okay with me.

☐ My goal is to serve Jesus Christ above all else.

☐ I love by the law of love rather than the letter of the law.

☐ I accept my human limitations, weaknesses, and failures, and I revel in God's grace for me.

☐ I respect my own boundaries as well as the boundaries of others.

☐ I trust God to work through my life in the decisions I make to steward it.

☐ I let go of toxic relationships while nurturing healthy relationships.

☐ I align myself with God's view of me.

☐ I accept the responsibility God gave me to steward my own life before Him.

☐ I live out the gospel of Jesus in the messiness of life on earth, applying grace where needed.

EMPOWERING YOURSELF

Write what the following statements mean to you, personally. How could your life change if you truly believed them to be true?

1. I don't need to be rescued. I need to be empowered. _____

_____

2. I can grow in tolerating the disapproval of other people. _____

_____

3. I can take responsibility for my own life. _____

_____

4. I can take back my dignity as a child of God. _____

_____

5. I can let go of my desire for things to be different and accept things the way they are. But I can also make my own decisions on what to do about that reality. _____

_____

_____

6. I can lean on the strength and endurance I've built up through years of being in a toxic relationship.

_____

_____

7. I can stand alone. _____

_____

_____

"If God is for us, who can be against us?...Who shall separate us from the love of Christ? Shall tribulation, or distress, or persecution, or famine, or nakedness, or danger, or sword? As it is written, 'For your sake we are being killed all the day long; we are regarded as sheep to be slaughtered.' No, in all these things we are more than conquerors through him who loved us. For I am sure that neither death nor life, nor angels nor rulers, nor things present nor things to come, nor powers, nor height nor depth, nor anything else in all creation, will be able to separate us from the love of God in Christ Jesus our Lord."

—Romans 8:31b, 35-39 (ESV)

PRAYER

Write your own prayer to God asking Him for direction and wisdom and help in learning and applying the skills we talked about in this chapter. Get specific. What areas do you struggle with the most? Talk to Him about those areas. His desire is to grow you into a strong and mighty Ezer Kenegdo. This is your destiny. When you pray for this, you are praying right into His will for you.

Dear Heavenly Father,

_____

_____

_____

_____

_____

_____

_____

_____

_____

_____

GROUP DISCUSSION QUESTIONS

1. Did anything shift in your beliefs or perspectives as a result of studying this chapter? If so, what was it?

_____

_____

_____

_____

2. How are you practicing or not practicing healthy boundaries in your own life?

_____

_____

_____

_____

3. In the Aiming for Authenticity exercise, what are two areas you are strong in and two areas where you need some tender loving care?

_____

_____

_____

_____

4. Do you want to be _rescued_ or _empowered_? Why?

_____

_____

_____

_____

Week Nine

HOUSE OF CARDS

"It's hard to tell who has your back, from who has it long enough just to stab you in it...."

NICOLE RICHIE

"Even if my father and mother abandon me, the LORD will hold me close."

PSALM 27:10 (NLT)

"Can a mother forget the baby at her breast
and have no compassion on the child she has borne?
Though she may forget, I will not forget you!
See, I have engraved you on the palms of my hands..."

ISAIAH 49:15-16

Reading Assignment

Chapter Nine: House of Cards

Summary Points:

1. When you set boundaries, people who want to control you AND people who don't have healthy boundaries themselves will not like your boundaries and will likely attack you.

2. Keeping a journal of the abuse cycle will help you pinpoint patterns you can use to figure out where boundaries are most necessary.

3. An abuser will follow a typical pattern of behavior when you set boundaries. He will get upset, feign an apology, make it look like he's changing, get sneakier with the abuse, get angrier when you continue to call him out, and then launch a smear campaign against you.

4. A church will typically side with the abuser because he is the one wanting to "save the marriage" which is the church's number one goal. If your goal is to get to a place of safety and sanity, they will call you out as the one "in the wrong." It is the rare church that does not follow this pattern.

5. Your emotionally and spiritually healthy friends and family will support you whatever you decide to do. The rest will throw you under the bus unless you do what THEY want you to do. This hurts, but it also reveals who your real friends are.

When you are finished with Workbook Chapter Nine you will:

- Understand what emotions are triggered in you when someone violates your boundaries.

- Be able to imagine possibilities for your future other than the one you may be currently resigned to.

- Know how to process an emotionally abusive incident so you can analyze it objectively.

- Recognize the behavior patterns both you and your partner display when conflict occurs.

- See the differences between safe relationships and unsafe relationships and how your body actually TELLS you what's going on even when your mind is trying to rationalize something completely different.

MINING FOR GOLD

1. What was the golden nugget you found in chapter nine? Write down a favorite quote or new idea.

_____

_____

_____

_____

2. What did you believe before you read this chapter?

_____

_____

_____

_____

3. How were your prior beliefs challenged in this chapter?

_____

_____

_____

_____

4. How will the golden nugget you discovered help your life look different ten years from now?

_____

_____

_____

_____

PROCESSING THE PATTERN

This is an exercise you can do over and over again in your journal. (I've included a copy of this in the appendix so you can make copies and fill it out each time you experience an incident.) Over time, it will help you find the patterns you need to see in order to break the cycle. You will want to do this exercise every time an emotionally charged incident happens in your relationship that leaves you feeling confused, angry, scared, or any other strong emotion. Not all the questions will apply every time. Answer the questions that do apply.

1. What led up to this incident? Think about the timeline of events and summarize them here.

_____

_____

_____

_____

_____

_____

_____

2. Who was involved—and what did they each want?

_____

_____

_____

_____

_____

_____

_____

_____

3. How did they each go about getting what they wanted?

_____

_____

_____

_____

_____

_____

_____

_____

_____

4. Describe each person's emotions as you perceived them.

_____

_____

_____

_____

_____

_____

_____

_____

_____

5. Did anyone say something to shut down the conversation or ignore someone else's perspective? If so, what did they say? What did they do? What was their body language communicating?

_____

_____

_____

_____

_____

_____

_____

_____

6. What was your response? What did you say? Do? What were you feeling? Why? Describe what your body was experiencing (shaking, clenched stomach, heart racing, etc.).

_____

_____

_____

_____

_____

_____

_____

_____

7. Was the problem resolved? Why or why not?

_____

_____

_____

_____

_____

_____

_____

_____

8. Is there anything you wish you would have done differently in the way you reacted or handled the situation? If you were to rewrite your part, how would it change? (Please be aware that even though you can change some of the ways you respond to abuse, you cannot change the abuse itself. You cannot control what your partner does. Any changes you make are for YOU, and you alone. They strengthen your inner world so you can begin to regain your inner dignity and voice.)

_____

_____

_____

_____

_____

_____

_____

_____

EMOTION CHECK

Look at the list below and circle the emotions you feel most when you set a boundary and it is disrespected or violated. You may need to think about a recent incident in order to recall some of those emotions.

Anger	Helpless	Cold
Frustration	Indifferent	Victimized
Anxiety	Stressed	Rejection
Sadness	Defensive	Insecure
Fear	Paralyzed	Heated
Indignation	Hurt	Annoyed
Shock	Withdrawn	Threatened
Vengeful	Disgusted	
Hopeless	Undone	

List anything else you feel: _____

_____

_____

At the beginning of chapter nine, you read about a fork in the road with two paths. Which one do you usually take and why? How does that road make you feel? _____

_____

_____

Imagine that you took the other path. What do you think would happen? How do you think you'd feel on that road? _____

_____

_____

WHAT THE ABUSER DOES

You can do this next exercise in retrospect, analyzing a past boundary violation, OR you can do this exercise in the present time, analyzing something that is currently happening, OR you can set up a new boundary and analyze what happens in the future when you do. The purpose here is to see how the pattern exists in your relationship—again, so you will be able to identify ways to change the cycle.

1. The Abuser Growls and Barks. Write down how your partner "growled" and "barked" at you when you set up a boundary. _____

_____

_____

How do you feel at this point? Guilty? Angry? Annoyed? Scared? Describe your emotions and thoughts.

_____

_____

2. The Abuser Feigns an Apology. Did your partner apologize? If so, did he fully own his behavior (growling and barking and violating your boundary) or did he minimize it? Justify it? Deny it? Put some of the blame on you for it? Did he expect forgiveness right away? Did he expect you to move on and be done with it? Was he able to be specific about what he did wrong, or did he generalize the behavior?

_____

_____

_____

How do you feel at this point? Guilty? Angry? Annoyed? Grateful? Relieved? Describe your emotions and thoughts. _____

_____

_____

_____

3. The Abuser Jumps Through Hoops. How has your partner tried to make it appear to those on the outside that he is cooperating? Changing? What are you seeing on the back end? _____

_____

_____

How are you feeling? Why do you think you feel that way? _____

_____

_____

4. The Abuser Gets Sneakier. What are some of the more hidden ways you're feeling shamed, blamed, and criticized? Do you feel guilty about anything? What? Why? Are those on the outside seeing real change? How do they know? _____

_____

_____

5. The Bully Shows Up. If you continue to maintain your boundaries, he will eventually get tired and start putting pressure on you to give up and let him be the way he is without any consequences. In what ways has your partner done this to you? _____

_____

_____

How does it make you feel? _____

_____

_____

_____

_____

6. **The Smear Campaign.** Have you experienced this yet? How has he smeared your reputation to those on the outside? _____

_____

_____

_____

_____

Who has chosen to believe him? Why do you think those particular people made that choice?_____

_____

_____

_____

_____

Who has chosen not to believe him? Why?_____

_____

_____

_____

_____

How do you feel about the smear campaign? Angry? Scared? Out of control? Why do you feel that way? What are you doing to take care of yourself while you're going through this? _____

_____

_____

_____

_____

YOUR CHURCH

You've had a chance to analyze what your church believes in chapter six. Here we are going to look at how your body is feeling and reacting to the things you are hearing and experiencing in your church. (If you no longer attend church, think about past experiences with church when doing this exercise.)

1. Do you feel warm and welcome and safe in your church? Or do you feel like you need to hide things? Why or why not?

    _____

    _____

2. God made our bodies and brains to work together in a complex way to give us helpful information about our environment. We are wise to pay attention to our bodies and not just our minds (thoughts). The next time you attend church, notice how your body feels. Describe what you are experiencing in your head, shoulders, back, chest, stomach, and abdomen.

    _____

    _____

3. Is there anything about your experiences in church that confuse you or give you a sense of being ill at ease or cautious? If so, what? And why do you think you feel that way?

    _____

    _____

4. What is your main motivation for going to church? Your kids? The belief that it's the right thing to do? The connections? The support? The things you learn there? The worship? Anything else?

    _____

    _____

5. In your own words, what is church for? What is the purpose of church? Where is The Church (global) of Jesus Christ? Who is The Church (global) of Jesus Christ? How does this give you hope?

    _____

    _____

FRIENDS AND FAMILY

In this exercise, we are going to look at some of the most significant people in your life and how they interact with you.

First go through and write down the names of some of the most important people in your life right now on the heading lines below.

Then, underneath each name, describe the role they have in your life along with two other things:

1. How they treat you when you are agreeing with them and making them feel good about themselves and their relationship with you and

2. How they treat you when you disagree or hold a different opinion than they do. You can write about their words, actions, and body language. See if you can pick up on some patterns.

Name: _____   **Role:** _____

Response 1: _____

_____

Response 2: _____

_____

Name: _____   **Role:** _____

Response 1: _____

_____

Response 2: _____

_____

Name: _____   **Role:** _____

Response 1: _____

_____

Response 2: _____

_____

_____

Name: _____   **Role:** _____

Response 1: _____

_____

Response 2: _____

_____

_____

Name: _____   **Role:** _____

Response 1: _____

_____

Response 2: _____

_____

_____

THINK ABOUT IT

1. Describe what you believe a safe (not perfect) person would be like. How would they behave? What would be important to them? How would they show up in their relationships? _____

_____

_____

_____

2. Do you have a safe (not perfect) person in your life? How do you know they are safe? Why do you feel you can trust them? _____

_____

_____

_____

3. Compare your safe person with Jesus. In what ways are they similar? _____

_____

_____

_____

4. Imagine what life would be like if everyone you were closest to was SAFE. Describe how things might be different for you. _____

_____

_____

_____

PRAYER

Say out loud:

Dear Heavenly Father,

Thank You that You have promised to never leave or forsake me. People will fail me, but You will never fail to love and care for me. Your faithfulness reaches to the heavens.

You are my Safe Tower I can run to when life feels unsafe. I can hide myself in the shadow of Your wings. You are my mother, my father, my sister, my brother, my friend. My identity, my origins, my core being are all rooted in You.

Thank you for Your wonderful creation of ME and my body! Thank you that my body and brain work together to give me important information about my environment and the people in it. Continue to teach me how to tap into this incredible resource provided by YOU.

Your Word says that Jesus didn't trust men because He knew what was in them. I appreciate knowing that it is okay not to just blindly trust anyone. That really, the only One I can fully trust is You. I want to keep growing in wisdom and understanding as I navigate my current and future relationships with people.

I want to be trustworthy, and I want to find others who are trustworthy. I want to be respectful of the personhoods of others, and I want to find others who will be respectful of mine.

It hurts to be betrayed. It hurts to lose people I've loved. People I thought loved me. People I thought I could trust. People I invested in and confided in. Every cell in my body screams in agony sometimes, and I wonder how I can bear it.

But You also experienced tremendous betrayal by Your friends and family. They invited You to a party and then murdered You. Your friends ran away. Everyone called You names. You were the Son of God, but they called You the son of the devil.

It is a comfort to know that YOU KNOW exactly how this feels. There are no easy answers or quick fixes. There is no drug that will make this pain go away. But I will sit with You in stillness, and I will rest on Your shoulder and believe that One Day all that is wrong will be made right again.

Lead me and guide me in Your Truth. I love You. I believe You. Help my lack of love and my lack of belief. You hold me even when I have no strength to hold on to You. For that, I know I will be eternally grateful one day.

In Jesus Name,

Amen

GROUP DISCUSSION QUESTIONS

1. What typically happens when you say "no" or set a boundary in your relationships? What do you do then, in response?

_____

_____

_____

_____

2. How have you experienced rejection or betrayal from your family of origin, your friends, or your church?

_____

_____

_____

_____

3. If you are comfortable doing so, share your Cycle exercise with your group along with any insights you gleaned from doing that exercise.

_____

_____

_____

_____

4. Tell your group about one safe person you have in your life and what makes them safe for you.

_____

_____

_____

_____

Week Ten

THE KEY TO YOUR FUTURE

"People are like stained-glass windows. They sparkle and shine when the sun is out, but when the darkness sets in their true beauty is revealed only if there is light from within."

ELISABETH KÜBLER-ROSS

"Therefore, if anyone is in Christ, the new creation has come: The old has gone, the new is here!"

II CORINTHIANS 5:17

"After all, no one ever hated their own body, but they feed and care for their body, just as Christ does the church—"

EPHESIANS 5:29

Reading Assignment

Chapter Ten: The Key to Your Future

Summary Points:

1. The process of healing is much like the process a caterpillar goes through to become a butterfly!

2. Self-care isn't selfish. It's critical to loving others and fulfilling the purpose God created us for. It's our God-given responsibility.

3. Self-advocacy means having healthy boundaries. It's what all healthy adults do, and it's necessary for healing.

4. Our core beliefs tell our brains what roads to drive over every day, and those roads dictate the direction we take in life. If we can change the roads, we can change our core beliefs, and that will change our lives.

5. Anger over the things people have done is normal. And forgiveness is letting go of your right to make things right while trusting God to do that on your behalf one day.

When You Are Finished With Workbook Chapter Ten You Will:

- Be able to identify what stage you're at in the healing process.

- Assess your current ability to advocate for yourself.

- Know how to rewire your brain.

- See the specific things that cause you anger.

- Understand where you are in the process of forgiving.

MINING FOR GOLD

1. What was the golden nugget you found in chapter ten? Write down a favorite quote or new idea.

_____

_____

_____

_____

2. What did you believe before you read this chapter?

_____

_____

_____

_____

3. How were your prior beliefs challenged in this chapter?

_____

_____

_____

_____

4. How will the golden nugget you discovered help your life look different ten years from now?

_____

_____

_____

_____

THE PROCESS OF HEALING

1. In this section of the book, which stage in the process do you think you are in currently? (You may be in several stages at once because the process isn't linear and clean; however, there is likely one stage that sticks out to you as the predominant stage you feel you're in right now.) _____

   • Denial (The caterpillar is hidden inside a tiny egg.)
   • Waking Up (The caterpillar is born!)
   • Learning (The caterpillar eats and eats!)
   • Grieving (The caterpillar goes into a chrysalis and begins transforming.)
   • Getting Out (The butterfly emerges.)
   • Rebuilding Faith and Friendships (The butterfly's wings dry and stretch out.)
   • New Life Begins (The butterfly spreads her wings and flies away!)

2. What has been the most painful part of each stage you've gone through so far? _____

   _____

   _____

   _____

   _____

   _____

   _____

   _____

3. What has been the most transformative and joyous part of each stage you've gone through so far?

   _____

   _____

   _____

   _____

   _____

4. What needs to happen in your current stage in order for you to move to the next stage?

_____

_____

_____

_____

_____

_____

_____

_____

5. What, specifically, do you think is the main thing holding you back from that next step, and why?

_____

_____

_____

_____

_____

_____

_____

_____

IMAGINE YOUR FUTURE

Close your eyes and pretend you are twenty years into the future. You are walking up to the home of the woman you will be in twenty years, and you're going to be invited in for a visit with her. Remember, this is the "NOW version of you" visiting YOURSELF twenty years in the future. Describe that woman's home. How does she decorate? What does she look like? Dress like? What kind of food does she serve you? What questions would you ask her? How would she respond? Write down your imaginary experience here with as much detail as possible. You'll be surprised at the kinds of insight and wisdom you have stored up inside you!

_____

_____

_____

_____

_____

_____

_____

_____

_____

_____

_____

_____

_____

_____

_____

SELF-CARE

1. What were you taught about self-care growing up? _____

_____

_____

_____

_____

2. Do you believe or FEEL deep inside that self-care is selfish and wrong? Why or why not?

_____

_____

_____

_____

3. How have you taken care of yourself in your destructive relationship? _____

_____

_____

_____

_____

4. How are you currently taking care of yourself? _____

_____

_____

_____

_____

Advocating for Yourself

How well do you advocate for yourself? Put a check mark by the statements that are true of you.

☐ I respect my own experience and voice.

☐ I forgive myself.

☐ I trust my gut.

☐ I am open to learning new things.

☐ I'm okay with making mistakes because that's how I learn and grow.

☐ I make my own choices.

☐ I feel comfortable changing my mind if I need to.

☐ I am willing to stand alone.

☐ I appreciate my strengths and accept my weaknesses.

☐ I spend time with healthy, wise people.

☐ I limit my time with toxic people.

☐ I don't try to justify or explain myself. I can tolerate the disapproval of others.

☐ I don't need the approval of others.

☐ I am good with ME!

Go to a mirror, look at yourself, and say OUT LOUD "_____, I will never, ever, EVER throw you under the bus again. From now on, I'm going to be your best human advocate. From now on I am going to love and accept you the way Jesus does. From now on I've got your back. You can count on me."

Was that hard for you to do? Why or why not?

_____

_____

_____

_____

_____

_____

CHALLENGE YOURSELF

1. Do the mirror exercise every morning until you really believe it!

2. One year from now, come back to the self-advocacy assessment and take it again. In what areas have you grown? What do you think contributed to your growth in those areas?

_____

_____

_____

_____

_____

_____

_____

_____

_____

_____

_____

_____

_____

_____

_____

Brain Renewal Exercise

This exercise, when done daily, has the power to actually rewire your brain. When your thoughts automatically turn to the destructive lies that were wired into you through your environment, family of origin, peers, culture, and religious systems, your emotions will get triggered in ways that impact your decision making and your relationships. On the flip side, when your thoughts automatically turn to the truth, your emotions will follow, and this will have a positive effect on your life.

If you can do this exercise first thing in the morning, even before you crawl out of bed, that would be ideal. The emotions that hit you in the morning when you first wake up often indicate where you are living in your head. This is the perfect time to grab those emotions, pin them down, and figure out what lies are attached to them.

Only pick one lie and one truth weapon to focus on for that day. If there are several of them, don't worry. They'll be waiting for you another day. Just focus on one thing at a time.

Keep in mind that it takes three to four weeks to destroy an old, rutted brain pathway and create a new one. Be patient with yourself and just focus on one pathway until it is rewired.

I've included a template in the Appendix for you to make copies of so you can do this exercise as many times as you need to. I've been rewiring for several years now, and it is a game-changer!

Step One: Emotion Dump

How do you feel? How does your body feel? Do you feel worried? Depressed? Angry? Stressed? Guilty? Powerless? Ashamed? Confused? Annoyed? Shocked? Scared? Worried? Disappointed? Regretful? Sad? Lonely? Jealous? Hopeless? Write whatever comes to mind.

_____

_____

_____

_____

_____

_____

_____

_____

Step Two: Brain Dump

What were you thinking about or what recently happened that brought about those feelings?

_____

_____

_____

_____

_____

_____

_____

_____

_____

_____

_____

_____

_____

_____

_____

_____

_____

_____

_____

_____

_____

Step Three: Identify the Lie Weapon

Notice the lie/lies you are believing. For example: "I'm worthless. I'm stupid. I should know better. I'll never change. I'll always be this way. I'm a bad person. I've failed my family." Write down all the things you are telling yourself about this situation.

_____

_____

_____

_____

_____

_____

_____

_____

Step Four: Pick Your Truth Weapon

What truth statement will you say to yourself 5-6 times today every time that negative thought or feeling sweeps over you? For example: "I made a mistake, but that's okay. I learned X,Y, and Z from it, and I'm growing!"

_____

_____

_____

_____

_____

_____

_____

_____

ANGER

Patrick Doyle teaches that below anger lies hurt.

1. Do you struggle with anger right now? If so, brainstorm below all the things that anger you (i.e. the things that have wounded you and continue to wound you).

I'll give you some ideas to get you started:

- I'm angry that my kids have to suffer.
- I'm angry that he gets away with lying.
- I'm angry that nobody believes me.
- I'm angry because I lost my friends.
- I'm angry because I sacrificed so much for nothing.

Now you try:

_____

_____

_____

_____

_____

_____

2. What are you currently doing about your anger, if anything? Has it helped? Why or why not?

_____

_____

_____

_____

_____

_____

_____

FORGIVENESS

1. What did you believe about forgiveness before you read this book? _____

_____

_____

_____

_____

_____

_____

2. *"Forgiveness is letting go of your right to make things right. Forgiveness is not letting the other person off the hook but rather letting him off your hook. He's still on God's hook! He doesn't owe you anything anymore. Now he owes God. You forgive his debt to you for taking all those things away, and now he stands before God with his debt."*

How does understanding forgiveness this way make a difference in how you feel or think about what has been done to you? _____

_____

_____

_____

_____

_____

_____

_____

_____

3. In your own words, write a letter of forgiveness to your abuser (you will NOT give this to him!) that is a reflection of what forgiveness means to you right now. Remember that forgiveness is a PROCESS. Not a "one and done" deal.

_____

_____

_____

_____

_____

_____

_____

_____

_____

_____

_____

_____

_____

_____

_____

_____

_____

_____

_____

PRAYER

Lord Jesus,

Thank you for giving me life and a future that doesn't just end when life on earth ends. It's so much bigger than that! Thank you that everything I learn and every way I grow during this short life here will carry through into eternity and serve to launch future creative endeavors and the fulfillment of Your plan in ways I can't even hope to comprehend right now.

In light of that, I am committed to growing in the following areas:

1. _____

_____

2. _____

_____

3. _____

_____

4. _____

_____

And to grow in those areas I am committed to doing the following things:

1. _____

_____

_____

2. _____

_____

_____

3. _____

_____

_____

_____

4. _____

_____

_____

_____

5. _____

_____

_____

_____

6. _____

_____

_____

_____

I know You will be with me as I grow in taking care of my body, my mind, my spirit, and my emotional health. You stand as my advocate, and You will train me to advocate for myself and others who are marginalized and powerless. You will bring the lies I am believing to my attention and help me replace those lies with the truth, and I am committed to creating new pathways in my brain and letting old pathways fade away. I let go of my right to hold my abuser accountable, and I give him over to You, knowing that You are faithful and just.

I choose to trust you with all of these things,

Amen

GROUP DISCUSSION QUESTIONS

1. Share what stage you're at in the healing process along with some of your highs and lows along the way.

   _____

   _____

   _____

2. Share what you learned from your future-self exercise.

   _____

   _____

   _____

3. What lie did you work to rewire this week and what was your truth weapon? Share any light-bulb moments you may have had. If the rewiring exercise was difficult for you, talk about why and see if your group members can help you with this.

   _____

   _____

   _____

4. Describe your struggle (or lack thereof) with anger and forgiveness. Where are you in that whole process? What do you think you still need in order to move forward in that area?

   _____

   _____

   _____

Week Eleven

WHAT COMES NEXT?

"We're always taught that God wants us to always only say 'I can't do this without You God', 'Whatever your will is God, that's my will too' but God says He is a father, and there is no good father who wants his children to have no will and to think that they can't stand on their own two feet. So maybe what you should be saying is 'I can do it' and 'I have a strong will, I know what I want.' When you think God's left you and wants you to be sitting like a duck, maybe He's actually believing in you, teaching you how to fly."

C. JoyBell C.

"See, I am doing a new thing!
Now it springs up; do you not perceive it?
I am making a way in the wilderness
and streams in the wasteland."

Isaiah 43:19

"And the God of all grace, who called you to his eternal glory in Christ, after you have suffered a little while, will himself restore you and make you strong, firm and steadfast."

I Peter 5:10

Reading Assignment

Chapter Eleven: What Comes Next?

Summary Points:

1. You don't need to be rescued. You need to be empowered.

2. Getting out and healing from emotional abuse is a long, terrifying, painful process. But it's worth it.

3. You don't have to walk that process alone.

When you are finished with workbook chapter eleven you will:

- Have a clear picture of what can happen to you if you decide to take steps toward freedom and healing.

- Understand that while it is hell to get out, women do it all the time, and there is hope and life on the other side of abuse.

MINING FOR GOLD

1. What was the golden nugget you found in chapter eleven? Write down a favorite quote or new idea.

_____

_____

_____

_____

2. What did you believe before you read this chapter?

_____

_____

_____

_____

3. How were your prior beliefs challenged in this chapter?

_____

_____

_____

_____

4. How will the golden nugget you discovered help your life look different ten years from now?

_____

_____

_____

_____

THE LADDER

In chapter eleven, you read about a ladder with ten hot rungs that leans against the wall of the pit of abuse. To get out of the pit, you have to climb the ladder, but the climb is going to hurt every step of the way. Let's look at the ladder more closely as it relates to your situation.

First Hot Rung: FEAR

Is your fear of staying greater than your fear of leaving? Or vice versa? Why? _____

_____

_____

What are you *most afraid of* if you stay? _____

_____

_____

What are you *most afraid of* if you leave? _____

_____

_____

Second Hot Rung: Trying to Get Your Abuser to Change

Do you believe your partner will change? If so, why? And how do you see it happening? _____

_____

_____

If you don't think this is a possibility, why not?_____

_____

_____

What do you think it would take to get you past this ladder rung? _____

_____

_____

Third Hot Rung: GRIEF Because Your Abuser Doesn't Actually Love You

Imagine that you have a daughter (even if you don't!), and she is getting married. How would you expect her husband to show her love in their relationship? Describe this love. _____

_____

_____

Now think of Jesus and His mother and disciples. How did Jesus show them love? Describe this love.

_____

_____

Now think of your partner. How does he show you love? _____

_____

_____

Compare/contrast his love with the other two descriptions above. _____

_____

_____

Do you feel loved? Why or why not? _____

_____

_____

Do you feel safe? Why or why not?_____

_____

_____

Do you feel honored? Why or why not? _____

_____

_____

Fourth Hot Rung: You Tell Someone, But They Don't Take You Seriously

Have you ever tried to explain your situation to anyone? Who? _____

_____

_____

What was their response? _____

_____

_____

Have you experienced the horror of not being taken seriously? Not being believed? How did that make you

feel? _____

_____

_____

Imagine you have an adult child who was violated in some way, but nobody believed him or her. What would

you offer to this child to show your love and care for him or her? What would you say or do? _____

_____

_____

Write a brief statement to yourself below in which you declare strong support for yourself and the truth of what you have experienced. Do this in the same way you would do this for your own child._____

_____

_____

Fifth Hot Rung: You Decide to Separate

Maybe you are not here yet. Maybe you aren't even close. That's okay. The process can take years, and some women choose to stay and work on growing stronger while remaining in the relationship. Only YOU know what is best for your life and the circumstances in which God has placed you. YOU get to decide. Nobody else makes that choice for you. They don't have to live your life. You do.

But let's imagine you do decide to take this step. What are some important things that you would need to do in order to prepare for a step like this? You could brainstorm your ideas in the following categories:

Finances _____

_____

_____

Housing _____

_____

_____

Custody Arrangements _____

_____

_____

Pets _____

_____

_____

Transportation _____

_____

_____

Job/Career _____

_____

_____

Sixth Hot Rung: You File for Divorce

This is a huge step. A dreaded step. Nobody wants to go here. It means the death and loss of so many things. A marriage. A family (as you know it). A home. A community. Friendships. Financial loss. Fear for your children. Loss of security. If you are the initiator, you are blamed for ending the marriage even though the abuse ended the marriage years before.

There are so many layers of painful things that happen once you file for divorce.

List some people in your life who have gone through divorce. _____

_____

_____

If you've had an opportunity to visit with them, what have you learned from their experiences? _____

_____

_____

Imagine that you can see yourself ten years from now, and you are divorced. What would your life look like?

_____

_____

What is the biggest hurdle for you personally when it comes to facing divorce as a possibility?_____

_____

_____

What would it take to overcome that hurdle? _____

_____

_____

Seventh Hot Rung: You are Rejected and Kicked Out

Have you experienced rejection as a direct result of disclosing anything about the nature of your relationship with your partner? What happened?_____

_____

_____

If you did file for divorce, how do you think your church would react? Would they support you or discipline you or something in between? _____

_____

_____

If the worst case scenario happened, and you were actually excommunicated from your church community, what would you do to take care of yourself and your spiritual health?_____

_____

_____

How do you think you would emotionally and spiritually survive that scope of rejection? _____

_____

_____

Eighth Hot Rung: Your Kids Suffer and Grieve

This is probably the worst fear a mother has. List your children below and their ages, and describe how you would predict they would react. Also list any risks each child would face as a result of a divorce.

1. _____

_____

2. _____

_____

3. _____

_____

4. _____

_____

5. _____

_____

6. _____

_____

7. _____

_____

8. _____

_____

Imagine each of them ten years down the road. How might a divorce make their lives different in a more positive way? _____

_____

_____

Ninth Hot Rung: You are Single and Alone

At this stage you're almost at the top, but you feel empty. You've lost your life as you once knew it, and you're starting over. You have to go through the grief process, and it takes a long time. It hurts.

Have you ever gone through the grief process before? Maybe with the death of a family member or friend? What do you know about this process from your personal experience? _____

_____

_____

Do you believe you can be okay by yourself? That you can be whole and complete without a partner? Without anyone else validating your existence? Why or why not? _____

_____

_____

What bothers you most about being alone? _____

_____

_____

What would need to happen in your life for you to really feel and believe and know, IN YOUR CORE, that you are whole and complete and loved in Christ? By yourself? _____

_____

_____

Tenth Hot Rung: You Have Health Problems

Survivors often have residual health issues from long term emotional abuse. Abuse puts a constant stress and strain on your health, and you may need to address some of those issues. Many women find that once they are out of the abusive relationship, their health improves tremendously.

Do you have any health problems that you suspect may be related to the stress of dealing with emotional abuse on a regular basis? What are those problems? _____

_____

_____

What have you done so far to address those health issues? _____

_____

_____

If you haven't addressed them, what is stopping you from doing so? _____

_____

_____

Imagine a life where you come home to peace and rest. To love and compassion. To beauty and quiet. How do you imagine your body and brain responding to this kind of life? _____

_____

_____

_____

_____

_____

_____

PRAYER

Dear Lord Jesus,

I don't know what the future holds for me, but I know that You will be with me no matter where I go. You will be with me even if others abandon me. I will never be alone, and I will find my tribe.

Thank you for the things I've learned working through this study. I'm curious about how it will cause inner shifts that will change the course of my life. I don't look forward to experiencing more pain, but I know that You will comfort me and show up for me in unexpected ways. Help me to find You in the daily battle. To feel Your nearness in the storms that are coming.

I choose to believe truth over lies.

I choose to believe that You are good, and You are powerful.

I choose to believe you are present, and You are Love to me.

I choose to believe I belong to You, and You will never forsake me.

I choose to believe I am beloved and worthy of love and respect because You created me.

I choose to believe the voice you gave me is my responsibility, and it is good.

I choose to believe I am okay even when others disagree or disapprove.

I choose to believe I can change, and change is good.

I choose to believe I am strong and getting stronger.

I choose to believe it is good to make mistakes and learn and grow.

I choose to let go of trying to control others and how they treat me, and instead I will control myself and how I treat myself.

I choose to let go of relationships that are harmful to my body and soul and mind and spirit.

I choose to follow YOU and not human beings.

Amen

Group Discussion Questions

1. You've made it to the end! What were your three biggest light bulb moments?

    _____

    _____

    _____

    _____

2. What do you plan to do moving forward to take care of yourself and your future? (Remember, baby steps are all that is required to go from point A to point B. Just baby steps!)

    _____

    _____

    _____

    _____

3. If you are on the ladder, which rung are you on, and how are you feeling about the climb so far? Confident? Terrified? Determined? Ready to give up?

    _____

    _____

    _____

    _____

4. What do you believe you need the most to move forward in your life at this point, and why?

    _____

    _____

    _____

    _____

Appendix

PROCESSING THE PATTERN

1. What led up to this incident? Think about the timeline of events and summarize them here.

_____

_____

_____

2. Who was involved and what did they each want?

_____

_____

_____

3. How did they each go about getting what they wanted?

_____

_____

_____

4. Describe each person's emotions as you perceived them.

_____

_____

_____

5. Did anyone say something to shut down the conversation or ignore someone else's perspective? If so, what did they say? What did they do? What was their body language communicating?

_____

_____

_____

6. What was your response? What did you say? Do? What were you feeling? Why? Describe what your body was experiencing (shaking, clenched stomach, heart racing, etc.).

_____

_____

_____

7. Was the problem resolved? Why or why not?

_____

_____

_____

8. Is there anything you wish you would have done differently in the way you reacted or handled the situation? If you were to rewrite your part, how would it change? (Please be aware that even though you can change some of the ways you respond to abuse, you cannot change the abuse itself. You cannot control what your partner does. Any changes you make are for YOU, and you alone. They strengthen your inner world so you can begin to regain your inner dignity and voice.)

_____

_____

_____

_____

_____

JOURNAL BRAIN REWIRING EXERCISE

REPLACING LIES WITH THE TRUTH

1. Think of a recent experience in which you believed something negative about yourself as a woman. Write down what you believed about yourself. (You can pick one of the statements you checked in the earlier exercise if you'd like.) _____

_____

_____

2. What did the different parts of your body feel when you believed that thing about yourself? What did your stomach feel? Your head? Your shoulders? Your back? Your chest? _____

_____

_____

_____

3. Describe your emotions when you were believing that thing. Were you anxious? Angry? Hopeless? Lonely? Fearful? Empty? Numb?_____

_____

_____

4. Look at your belief and rewrite it so it says the OPPOSITE of what it says now. For example, if you wrote: "I believed I had no right to express pain about what my husband did to me because I was also imperfect and a sinner." You would re-write it like this: "I do have a right to express pain about what my husband does to me because I am human and have feelings and needs that are just as important as anyone else's."

_____

_____

_____

_____

Resource Recommendations

Since the publication of *Is It Me?* in 2018, I've been exposed to more helpful resources. The list below references resources not mentioned in the first publication of *Is It Me?*

- *When Dad Hurts Mom* by Lundy Bancroft

- *Brain Talk* by Dr. David Schnarch

- *Broken Trust* by R. Remy Diederich

- *Boundaries for Your Soul* by Alison Cook PhD

- *Healing the Shame that Binds You* by John Bradshaw

- *Homecoming: Reclaiming and Healing Your Inner Child* by John Bradshaw

- *The Betrayal Bond: Breaking Free of Exploitive Relationships* by Patrick J. Carnes, PhD

- *The Search for Significance* by Robert S. McGee

- *Daughter Detox* by Peg Streep

ONGOING SUPPORT

I offer the following resources for women of faith dealing with destructive relationships.

- **A website full of supportive and educational articles** written with you in mind: https://flyingfreenow.com.

- **The Flying Free weekly podcast** which you can listen to on your favorite podcast app OR you can access it on my website: https://flyingfreenow.com/podcast. You can download beautiful transcripts of each episode if you prefer to read. I interview emotional abuse advocates, authors, speakers, and survivors on a number of relevant issues.

You can also connect with me on social media:

Facebook:	https://www.facebook.com/flyingfreenow
Twitter:	https://twitter.com/FlyFreeNatalie
Instagram:	https://www.instagram.com/nataliehoffmanflyingfree
YouTube:	https://www.youtube.com/flyingfree

I also offer a private education and support group with monthly courses, expert workshops, private Facebook groups, Butterfly stories, annual retreats, videos, and live events where we connect every month. I'd love to have you join this incredible community of women just like you! Visit www.joinflyingfree.com

Made in the USA
Las Vegas, NV
19 November 2020

11144176R00109